Essential Skills

Revised Edition

About the Cover

The breeze was fresh this bright day in May, and gaily-colored kites appeared like spring swallows, darting across the blue sky over Rhode Island's Narragansett Bay. Photographer Tony Botelho was there to capture on film the kite-flights of Christy Menard, Art Pelosi, Danny Champagne, Peggy Hulsey, John Rathjen, Jack Christie, Stephen Jencks, Marion Alig and Megen Mills.

A salute to the rowboaters who retrieved the "diamond-spinnaker" kite that got away! The errant kite shook in the wind like a wet dog and rejoined the others in the sky, completing the composition of the photograph on the covers of the *Essential Skills Series.*

The six kites symbolize the higher levels of comprehension gained through mastery of skills from the six essential categories of comprehension.

About the Illustrations

Many of the pictures illustrating the passages in the *Essential Skills Series* were reproduced from the following books in the *Dover Pictorial Archive Series*, Dover Publications, Inc., New York: *Treasury of Art Nouveau, Design and Ornament*, Carol Belanger Grafton; *Harter's Picture Archive for Collage and Illustration*, Jim Harter; and *Animals: A Pictorial Archive from Nineteenth-Century Sources*, Jim Harter.

Other illustrations are by Deborah Christie, Howard Lewis and Thomas Ewing Malloy.

Essential Skills Series

4B
Kruger

Essential Skills Book 4

Walter Pauk, Ph.D.
Director, Reading Research Center
Cornell University

Revised Edition

Jamestown Publishers
Providence, Rhode Island

Essential Skills Series
No. 304, Book 4

Cover Design by Deborah Hulsey Christie, adapted from the Original Design by Stephen R. Anthony

Text Design by Deborah Hulsey Christie

Printed in the United States

AL   84 85 86 9 8 7 6 5 4

ISBN 0-89061-223-4

Preface

Practice Makes Perfect

Why do some students shoot baskets over and over again and others skate and reskate the same routine? These beginners know that practice makes perfect. Not only do beginners know this, but pros do too. For what other reason do they work at baseball and football week after week before the opening dates?

Value of Practice

The pros know the value of practice, but they also know the value of something else. They know that practice without *instruction* and *guidance* does not automatically lead to improvement. That's why they have the best coaches that money can buy.

And so it is with developing the skills of reading. There must be the right kind of practicing and the right kind of coaching.

First, a word about practice. In this book the right kind of practice is provided by twenty-five highly interesting and carefully selected passages. Here is material enough on which to grow and keep growing.

Value of Coaching

Now about coaching! Good coaching takes the form of instruction and guidance. In this book the instruction is straightforward and uncomplicated. It puts you directly on the right track, and better still, you are kept on the right track by two unusual systems of guidance. The first system is the uniquely designed, six-way question format which makes sure that every ounce of practice is directed toward improvement. Nothing is wasted!

Diagnostic Chart

The second system of guidance is the Diagnostic Chart. This chart is no ordinary gimmick. In truth, it provides the most dignified form of diagnosis and guidance yet devised. It provides instantaneous and continuous diagnosis and gentle but certain self-guidance. It yields information directly to the student. This form of self-guidance leads to the goal of all education: the goal of self-teaching.

Acknowledgments   Now, I want to make some acknowledgments, especially to the students who were the guinea pigs. Afterwards I told them so, but they said, "We didn't mind even then. And now that it is over, we're all the happier because we know how much we've learned." But what the students did not know was how much I learned from them. For this I thank them all, class after class.

I direct especial thanks to Linda Browning, Anita DuBose, and Karen Duddy for handling the almost countless number of selections, writing and refining the questions and making sure that the series kept moving: all, a most demanding task.

Finally, I am most grateful to authors, editors and publishers who have generously given permission to quote and reprint in this book from works written and published by them. The books quoted in the text and used as sources of reading extracts are listed in the back of the book.

Walter Pauk

Contents

To the Instructor

All of us believe in this truism: to learn to read, a person must read. But, placing a book in front of a student won't automatically promote reading.

This last sentence brings up another truism: you can lead a horse to water, but you can't make it drink. To tempt a horse, the water must be clear, cool and clean.

To tempt the student, the passages must be genuinely fascinating. Knowing this, we packed each book with twenty-five "I can't put the book down" type of passages.

Each passage had to meet at least the following criteria: *high interest level, appropriate readability level* and *factual accuracy of contents.* High interest was assured by choosing passages from popular magazines that appeal to a wide range of readers. The readability level of each passage was assessed by applying Dr. Edward B. Fry's *Formula for Estimating Readability,* thus enabling the arrangement of passages on a single grade level within each book. The factual accuracy of the passages is high because they were written by professional writers whose works are recognized and respected.

The Great Value of Questions

Dr. Mortimer J. Adler says that the overall secret for improving one's reading can be boiled down to knowing how to keep awake while reading. He means more than keeping one's eyes open. He means keeping one's mind open and active.

One sure-fire way to do this is to keep trying to answer questions while reading. Questions not only keep one's mind awake, but also keep the mind active, not letting it get flabby. Here's a good story that makes the same point.

> To keep their fish alive for the fresh-fish markets, the owners of fishing boats used a water-filled floating tank. The fish remained alive all right, but they were never firm, always flabby. One captain, however, always brought back firm, fresh, active fish. His fish always received a higher price.

One day he revealed his secret: "You see," he said, "for every hundred herrings I put into my tank, I put in one catfish. It is true that the catfish eat five or six of the herrings on the trip back to port, but the catfish keep the rest alert and constantly active. That's why my herring arrive in beautiful condition."

The work of the catfish, in this book, is done by the six essential questions (subject matter, supporting details, conclusion, clarifying devices, vocabulary in context, and main idea). These questions keep the minds of students alert, active and in beautiful condition.

The main idea questions in this book are not the usual multiple-choice variety. Given four statements, the students are asked to recognize the main idea of the passage. They also tell why each of the other three does not express the main idea; the students identify one statement as too narrow, one as too broad and one as merely a detail.

By asking these six types of questions in each passage, students quickly learn to read with a questioning and anticipating attitude. This attitude, necessary for high comprehension, is easily transferred to other material such as the textbook.

The Diagnostic Chart

Those who used the first edition of these books had high praise for the Diagnostic Chart. In sum, this is what they said.

> The Diagnostic Chart is truly ingenious because it is, in fact, a self-diagnosing instrument. The Chart instantly, simply and continually shows students their strengths and weaknesses.

Here is how the Chart works. The six questions for each passage are always in the same order. For example, the question designed to teach the skill of making *conclusions* is always in the number three position, and the question designed to teach the

9

skill of identifying *clarifying devices* is always in the number four position, and so forth. This innovation of keeping the questions in order sets the stage for the smooth functioning of the Chart.

The Chart works automatically when the letters of the answers are placed in the spaces on the Chart. Even after completing one passage, the Chart will reveal the type or types of questions answered correctly as well as the types answered incorrectly. But more important, the Chart will identify the types of questions missed consistently. More persuasive identification is possible after three or more passages have been completed. By then, a pattern can be observed. For example, if the answers to question number three (making conclusions) are incorrect for all three passages, or on three out of four, then this weakness shows up automatically.

Once a weakness is revealed, instruct the students to take the following steps: First, turn back to the instructional pages to study the section in which the topic is discussed. Second, go back to read again the questions in that particular category that were missed; then, with the correct answers in mind, read the entire passage again, trying to see how the author developed the answers to the questions. Third, on succeeding passages, put forth extra effort to answer correctly the questions in that particular category. Fourth, if the difficulty still persists, arrange for a conference with the instructor.

To the Student

How do readers get the meaning from written words? To get meaning, readers need to know at least six essential skills.

1. Subject Matter — Readers need to know how to concentrate or focus on the writing. This helps them learn what the writing is about.
2. Main Idea — Readers need to know how to grasp the main idea or point of the writing.
3. Supporting Details — Readers need to be able to connect supporting details to the ideas.
4. Conclusions — Readers should be able to come to conclusions or guess endings based on the ideas.
5. Clarifying Devices — Readers should be able to note the writer's methods of making the points clear and alive.
6. Vocabulary in Context — Readers must know what the words in the writing mean.

Let's take a closer look at these six skills.

**Concentration/
Subject Matter**

One thing readers often say is, "I can't concentrate!" But there is a sure, fast cure. There is no better way to gain concentration when reading than this. Read the first few lines. Then ask yourself these questions: "What is this passage about?" "What is the subject matter?"

If you don't ask these questions, here's what may happen. Your eyes will move across the lines of print. Yet your mind will be thinking of other things.

But if you ask the questions, you will most likely get an answer, thus achieving concentration. Let's see if this method works. Here are the first lines of a passage:

> Wood ducks are the most beautiful ducks in North America. Once they were rare. Now — if you have sharp eyes and can keep quiet — you might see them in almost any woodland along streams and ponds.

After reading this, you can see that the author will talk about the wood duck. Now that your mind is on the trail, the chances are good it will follow the author's idea line by line. Thus, you will *concentrate* on the building of the subject matter.

Let's try the method again. Here are a few lines from another passage:

> Of all the little animals in the world, the Columbian ground squirrel is one of the liveliest and friendliest. It is nicknamed "picket pin." This is because it sits as stiff and straight as a stake in the ground.

Again, you most likely had no trouble picking out the subject. It is the Columbian ground squirrel.

Main Idea

Once the subject matter has been grasped, it is time for the next question. Ask yourself, "What is the author's main idea?" "What point is the passage trying to make?"

With such questions in mind, you can be sure an answer will often pop up. But when no questions are asked, all things seem the same. Nothing stands out. The reader will not see the point of the passage.

Let's look at another passage. This time we will find the main idea.

> Wood ducks never nest on the ground as most ducks do, but in a big hole in a tree. Trees with big holes in them are hard to find.

You don't have the full passage to read, so I will tell you the answer. The main point is that with fewer and fewer old, dead trees with big holes in them, we will have fewer and fewer wood ducks.

Thus, when questions are asked, the reader is acting upon the content. Reading becomes a two-way street with both reader and writer engaged. In a sense, the reader talks with the author. So the passage comes to life. Reading then is a joy.

Supporting Details

Do we like details? Of course we do. In long pieces of writing, main ideas are like the bones. They are the skeleton of the writing. The details are the flesh. They give the writing fullness and life.

Details are used to support the main ideas. So the term *supporting details* fits well. These supporting details come in many forms. The most common forms are examples, definitions, comparisons, contrasts, repetitions and descriptions.

The author of "The Wood Duck" lets us know that the passage is about wood ducks. Next, the author makes sure we learn that the point is that without trees with holes, the wood duck will not nest. Thus, there would be fewer wood ducks.

Now that we are involved in this problem, the author gives us details on how we can provide trees with holes in them. The author *describes* how we can build a wood duck nesting box. Here's the excerpt:

> Why don't you and your parents put up a wood duck nesting box right now? It would be about two feet (about .61 meters) high and ten inches (about 25.4 centimeters) square. Make the entry hole about four inches (about 10.2 centimeters) across. Use rough lumber on the inside, so the ducklings can climb up the sides to the hole. Put wood shavings on the bottom. In these the duck will lay her eggs. To keep her eggs warm, she covers them with her own feathers. If you can't find a tree near the water, you will need a post. Place the box ten to thirty feet (about 3.1 to 9.1 meters) high.

You can see in the above passage how important details are in telling a story. Details let the reader see what's going on. They paint a vivid picture of the action. They may tell how to do something. They may tell how something happened.

In long passages there will also be sub-ideas. It is important to be careful not to mistake a sub-idea for a main idea. Sub-ideas are broader than details. But sub-ideas are still not the main point. The main idea has to do with the whole passage. The sub-idea has to do with just part of it. Note that in the next sample, the sub-idea is about the food that wood ducks eat. The whole passage is not about food. Thus, food is *not* the main idea. For the most part, you will see that a sub-idea takes the space of one paragraph. Often, the topic sentence of the paragraph is a statement of a sub-idea.

The following excerpts show how the author groups and structures supporting details around the sub-ideas that are stated in topic sentences. A sub-idea will hold a group of details together.

> Wood ducks eat acorns and all kinds of nuts. Their stomachs (or gizzards) have strong muscles. They can break the hardest nuts, some that you could barely crack with a hammer, in their stomachs. Wood ducks like berries, duckweed and insects. But best of all they like to eat spiders. That's ice cream to them.

The topic sentence is the first sentence. It states that the sub-idea is the foods wood ducks eat. Next, the author describes how the newly hatched ducklings get down to the ground from the nest.

Here are more details grouped around a sub-idea.

> Sometimes they nest in holes up in trees that are twice as high as a flagpole. Just think, the baby ducklings must jump to the ground the day they hatch. They don't get hurt, though, because they're light, like little puffs of cotton. The mother stands at the foot of the tree and calls and calls. The ducklings peek out of the hole. Then, like little paratroopers, they jump quickly, one right after the other, to join their mother. She must then hurry them to the pond where they're safe.

Thus, one of the main jobs of *supporting details* is to give some fullness to the passage. The passage would be just a boring, skimpy statement of the main idea with its bare-boned sub-ideas if not for details. The details give the passage life.

Conclusion   The reader will move through a passage, grasping the main and sub-ideas and their details. It is then common for the reader to start to guess a conclusion or ending to the story. Such guesses are part of the sport of reading. Often, the author gives the reader an ending. In such a case, the joy of reading lies in the fact that the reader finds out the guess was right. But the ending may not be given. The reader then will try to guess the ending that is hinted by the author.

The conclusion from the excerpts just read about the wood duck is in having the reader see the pleasure of observing a wood duck. The final sentence is this:

> If you're lucky, though, and if your (duck) house is in place before the ice melts, you will have a wood duck family in the summer.

In a passage called "From Pond to Prairie," the author has this conclusion:

> Finally, there is no longer much open water. The pond has disappeared. Depending on the kinds of plants that have filled it, the pond may be called a bog or a marsh. As changes continue for many more years, the bog may become a forest.

The skillful reader is like a detective. This reader follows the story, always thinking, "Where is the author leading me?" "What's the final point?" "What's the conclusion?" And the reader, like a detective, must try to guess the conclusion, changing the guess if necessary as the story unfolds.

Clarifying Devices   The author uses clarifying devices to make the points in the story clear and alive. In a sense, the *topic sentence* may be thought of as a clarifying device. It is often placed at the start of a paragraph. In this way, the author gives the reader a quick point of focus.

The point of the passage becomes clear after reading it.

But more often, by clarifying devices, we mean the literary devices in the passage. These are words or phrases which keep the ideas, sub-ideas and details in clear focus and in order.

Authors use literary devices to make details clear and interesting. An example of a device is the *metaphor,* as in "But best of all they like to eat spiders. *That's ice cream to them.*"

One more literary device is the *simile.* "*Like little paratroopers,* they (the ducklings) jump quickly, one right after the other, to join their mother," is a simile. The simile helps the reader imagine a vivid scene. It brings to the mind of the reader something known — paratroopers. Then it compares the known idea to the ducklings' jump from their nest to make a fresh, new idea. It is fun to imagine the little ducks copying real paratroopers jumping from a plane.

Besides metaphors and similes, other *clarifying devices* are organizational patterns. One common pattern is to unfold the events in the order of time. Thus, one thing happens first and then another and another, and so forth.

The time pattern orders the event. The event may take place in the span of five minutes. It may last hundreds of years. A time pattern may be used to relate the habits of an animal from its birth to its death.

You should learn to find these literary devices. They help you to understand the passage and speed your reading.

Vocabulary in Context

A reader who does not know what the author's words mean may not understand the passage. A reader should look up in the dictionary the unknown words.

Also a reader may understand only the general meaning of the word. But sometimes a more *exact* meaning is needed to grasp the passage fully. A reader who places a general meaning on a word may end up with a blurred picture of the idea. An exact meaning will give the reader a full and clear picture.

For instance, in the next excerpt are two common words that many people feel they already know. Thus, they don't see the need to look them up in the dictionary. But few people know the exact meaning of these words.

> Depending on the kinds of plants that have filled it, the pond may be called a *bog* or a *marsh*.

Do you know the difference between a bog and a marsh? Is there a difference? If so, what is it? How would your mental picture change if you knew?

Looking up words for their exact meanings is rewarding. A precise vocabulary leads to true understanding.

You may find it troublesome to look up words you feel you already know. But you should get into this habit to improve your reading. Of course, words you do not know must always be looked up. You would most likely need a dictionary for these words:

> Nothing could appear more *benign* than a field aglow with daisies, goldenrod and Queen Anne's lace.

> *Sphinxlike,* it crouches among the flowers until the desired insect wanders within reach.

The dictionary is like a stock market. Here you exchange fuzzy meanings for exact meanings. You get new meanings for unknown words. All this is at no cost. It takes just a flip of your finger.

Answering the Main Idea Question

To be able to find the main idea of the things you read is important. It is one of the best reading skills you can learn. The main idea questions in this book are not the ones you've seen where you pick just the right answer. Instead, each main idea question is made up of four statements. Two of the statements refer to just parts of the passage. One of these is a *detail*. It states a point. But that point has little to do with the passage as a whole. The next statement is *too narrow*. It tells more than the detail statement. Still, it's too specific to tell about the main point of the passage. The "too narrow" statement is often a sub-idea.

The last two statements deal with the whole passage. One is *too broad*. It is too general and too vague to be a good main idea statement. The final statement is the *main idea*. It tells *who* or *what* the point of the passage is. The main idea statement answers the question *does what?* or *is what?* also.

Read the sample passage below. Then follow the instructions in the box. The answer to each part of the main idea question has been filled in for you. The score for each answer has also been marked.

Sample

The steel trap's jaws had caught the coyote midway across the foot. The pain must have been awful. Yet the coyote never stopped trying to tear loose. It had dug a circle about six inches (about 15.2 centimeters) deep, stretching the full length of the steel chain.

Two young boys out hiking saw this trapped coyote. They hurried to a nearby ranch. The ranch owner heard them out and came to help.

They held the coyote's neck down firmly with hoe handles. Then they opened the trap's jaws. The coyote slipped free. But the animal stayed there, just looking at its helpers. Perhaps it was wondering what makes some people demons and others saints.

The animal had to be gently nudged before it would leave. At last, it hobbled off a short distance. Then it turned, pausing to look again at the good people who had spared its life.

	Answer	Score
Mark the main idea	M	10
Mark the statement that is a detail	D	5
Mark the statement that is too narrow	N	5
Mark the statement that is too broad	B	5

a. Two young boys helped to free a trapped coyote.
[This statement is one that gathers all the important points. It gives a correct picture of the main idea in a brief way: (1) two young boys, (2) a trapped coyote, and (3) freeing it.]

M   10

b. Kind hearts set free a doomed coyote.
[This statement is too broad. It doesn't state *who* set the coyote free. It doesn't tell *why* it was doomed.]

B   5

c. Hoe handles were used to hold the coyote down.
[This is just one of many details found in the passage. It has little to do with the passage as a whole.]

D   5

d. A steel trap was opened to set a coyote free.
[Opening the trap is *part* of the main idea. But any main idea statement must give the chief actors credit. It must mention the two boys who set the coyote free.]

N   5

Getting the Most Out of This Book

The following steps could be called "tricks of the trade." Your teachers might call them "rules for learning." It doesn't matter what they are called. What does matter is that they work.

Think About the Title

A famous language expert told me a "trick" to use when I read. "The first thing to do is to read the title. Then spend a few moments thinking about it."

Writers spend much time thinking up good titles. They try to pack a lot of meaning into them. It makes sense, then, for you to spend a few seconds trying to dig out some meaning. These few moments of thought will give you a head start on a passage.

Thinking about the title can help you in another way, too. It helps you concentrate on a passage before you begin reading. Why does this happen? Thinking about the title fills your head full of thoughts about the passage. There's no room for anything else to get in to break concentration.

The Dot System

Here is a method that will speed up your reading. It also builds comprehension at the same time.

Spend a few moments with the title. Then read *quickly* through the passage. Next, without looking back, answer the six questions by placing a dot in the box next to each answer of your choice. The dots will be your "unofficial" answers. For the main idea question (question six), place your dot in the box next to the statement that you think is the main idea.

The dot system helps by making you think hard on your first, *fast* reading. The practice you gain by trying to grasp and remember ideas makes you a stronger reader.

The Check-Mark System

You have now answered all of the questions with a dot. Next, read the passage once more *carefully*. This time, make your final answer to each question with a check mark (✓). Go to each question. Then, place a check mark in the box next to the answer of your choice. The answers with the check marks are the ones that will count toward your score.

Now answer the main idea question. Follow the steps that are on the question page. Use a capital letter to mark your final answer to each part of the main idea question.

The Diagnostic Chart

Now move your final answers to the Diagnostic Chart on page 102. Use the column of boxes under number *1* for the answers to the first passage. Use the column of boxes under number *2* for the answers to the second passage, and so on.

Write the letter of your answer in the *upper* part of each block.

Correct your answers using the Answer Key on pages 100 and 101. When scoring your answers, do *not* use an *x* for *incorrect* or a *c* for *correct*. Instead, use this method. If your choice is correct, make no mark in the lower part of the answer block. If your choice is *in*correct, write the letter of the correct answer in the *lower* part of the block.

Thus, the answer column for each passage will show your incorrect answers. And it will also show the correct answers.

Your Total Comprehension Score

Go back to the passage you have just read. If you answered a question incorrectly, draw a line under the correct choice on the question page. Then write your score for each question in the circle provided. Add the scores to get your Total Comprehension Score.

Graphing Your Progress

After you have found your Total Comprehension Score, turn to the Progress Graph on page 103. Write your score in the box under the number for each passage. Then put an *x* along the line above the box to show your Total Comprehension Score. Join the *x*'s as you go. This will plot a line showing your progress.

Taking Corrective Action

Your incorrect answers give you a way to teach yourself how to read better. Take the time to study your wrong answers.

Go back to the question page. Read the correct answer (the one you have underlined) several times. With the correct answer in mind, go back to the passage itself. Read to see why the approved answer is better. Try to see where you made your mistake. Try to figure out why you chose a wrong answer.

The Steps in a Nutshell

Here's a quick review of the steps to follow. Following these steps is the way to get the most out of each *Essential Skills* book. Be sure you have read and understood all of the "To the Student" section on pages 11 through 22 before you start.

1. **Think About the Title of the Passage.** Try to get all the meaning the writer put into it.
2. **Read the Passage Quickly.**
3. **Answer the Questions, Using the Dot System.** Use dots to mark your unofficial answers. Don't look back at the passage.
4. **Read the Passage Again — Carefully.**
5. **Mark Your Final Answers.** Put a check mark (✓) in the box to note your final answer. Use capital letters for each part of the main idea question.
6. **Mark Your Answers on the Diagnostic Chart.** Record your final answers in the upper blocks of the chart on page 102.
7. **Correct Your Answers.** Use the Answer Key on pages 100 and 101. If an answer is not correct, (a) write the correct answer in the lower block, beneath your wrong answer. Then (b) go back to the question page. Place a line under the correct answer.
8. **Find Your Total Comprehension Score.** Find this by adding up the points you earned for each question.
9. **Graph Your Progress.** Mark and plot your scores on the graph on page 103.
10. **Take Corrective Action.** Read your wrong answers. Read the passage once more. Try to figure out why you were wrong.

Passages and Questions

1. A Warning From the Past

At the time of the finding of King Tut's tomb, the newspapers ran a strange story. The story was that King Tut had uttered a <u>curse</u>. The curse was that anyone who would touch his tomb would die. This curse was made to scare off grave robbers. Little did King Tut know that his curse would fall on good people.

At first, people joked about it. But in less than four months, it was no longer a joke. Lord Carnarvon, one of the two men who opened the tomb, was dead. A mosquito bit him. The bite turned red, then green, and soon Lord Carnarvon was dead.

Another strange thing happened. At the very same time that Lord Carnarvon died, his hound back in England howled, rolled over and died.

Later, an expert from Paris came to King Tut's tomb. Right there he died of a stroke. Soon another expert from New York City died when he, too, had visited the tomb. The idea of a curse was not laughed at again.

In all, twenty-two people who had played a part in the digging or in keeping the treasures have died. Even in modern times, strange things are still happening. In 1967, for instance, the man who signed the papers to get King Tut's treasure to Paris for a show died. He was hit by a car and killed.

Then, when the treasures reached Paris, an expert there was also hit and killed by a car. He had just looked at the show. Only a few years ago, Dr. Gamal Mehrez, the man in charge of the treasures in Cairo, died of a stroke. The pieces were still being packed to be shipped to London. After twenty-two deaths, no one jokes about the deadly power of King Tut's curse.

?

		Possible Score	Your Score

1. This passage is about

   ☐ a. an untold prayer.
   ☐ b. the discovery of a tomb.
   ☐ c. the treasures of King Tut.
   ☐ d. King Tut's Curse.   (15)   ◯

2. Lord Carnarvon's death was the result of a

   ☐ a. stroke.
   ☐ b. mosquito bite.
   ☐ c. car accident.
   ☐ d. fall.   (15)   ◯

3. Perhaps King Tut's curse

   ☐ a. is just for Egyptians.
   ☐ b. died with him.
   ☐ c. should be taken seriously.
   ☐ d. was just a rumor.   (15)   ◯

4. At first the curse was thought of as a

   ☐ a. joke.
   ☐ b. secret.
   ☐ c. mistake.
   ☐ d. prediction.   (15)   ◯

5. A curse as used in this passage means

   ☐ a. a blessing.
   ☐ b. a magic spell.
   ☐ c. a prayer.
   ☐ d. an order.   (15)   ◯

6. Main Idea

	Answer	Score
Mark the main idea	M	10
Mark the statement that is a detail	D	5
Mark the statement that is too narrow	N	5
Mark the statement that is too broad	B	5

a. Soon after opening King Tut's tomb, Lord Carnarvon died.

b. Lord Carnarvon died after being bitten by a mosquito.

c. The curse of King Tut has led to many mysterious happenings.

d. A curse is not always something to laugh at.

Total Comprehension Score
(Add your scores and enter the
total on the graph on page 103.)

Categories of Comprehension Questions

No. 1: Subject Matter	No. 4: Clarifying Devices
No. 2: Supporting Details	No. 5: Vocabulary in Context
No. 3: Conclusion	No. 6: Main Idea

2. What a Way To Treat a Friend

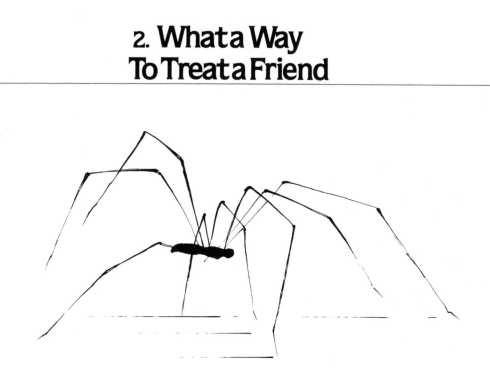

If all spiders suddenly disappeared, we'd starve to death within a very few months. We'd starve just as soon as our supplies of canned and frozen foods were used up. Then there would be no more food. There would be no more food because the millions and millions of insects would destroy all our crops and pastures. We just don't understand what spiders do for us.

Spiders eat mountains and mountains of insects. They are on the job both day and night. Spiders have eaten far more than the weight of all the three billion people on earth today.

These figures are hard to believe because we don't know just how many spiders there are. By taking samples of the earth, scientists have found that there are from one million to over two million spiders on an acre (about .4 hectares) of rough grassland.

Another interesting thing about spiders is that they live under all kinds of conditions. Spiders are found 22,000 feet (about 6,710 meters) up on our highest mountains living among the rocks, snow and ice. In the other direction, spiders by the hundreds are found 2,000 feet (about 610 meters) down in mines. In between, some live in birds' nests and in the nests of squirrels and even mice.

Spiders are not in competition with people for the same food. Spiders never eat vegetables. They always eat insects. Out of the 50,000 kinds of spiders in the world, less than a dozen can harm us. And then, it is because we step on them or put our hands in their nests. They never come to attack people. Spiders have no teeth. Most of them can't even break the skin of a person.

So, it is true that our very lives depend on the spider, yet we think nothing of taking its life. What a way to treat a friend!

	Possible Score	Your Score

1. This passage is about

   ☐ a. the black widow spider.
   ☐ b. insects.
   ☐ c. helpful spiders.
   ☐ d. poisonous spiders.

   Possible Score: 15

2. Spiders eat only

   ☐ a. plants.
   ☐ b. wood.
   ☐ c. insects.
   ☐ d. other spiders.

   Possible Score: 15

3. More spiders would mean

   ☐ a. less food for people.
   ☐ b. poorer soil.
   ☐ c. better crops.
   ☐ d. more harmful insects.

   Possible Score: 15

4. Spiders eat mountains and mountains of insects. This shows that

   ☐ a. spiders are poisonous.
   ☐ b. spiders have big appetites.
   ☐ c. spiders die easily.
   ☐ d. spiders eat vegetables.

   Possible Score: 15

5. Rough grassland is land that is

   ☐ a. swampy.
   ☐ b. wild and grass covered.
   ☐ c. wooded and uncut.
   ☐ d. hilly.

   Possible Score: 15

6. Main Idea

	Answer	Score
Mark the main idea	M	⑩
Mark the statement that is a detail	D	⑤
Mark the statement that is too narrow	N	⑤
Mark the statement that is too broad	B	⑤

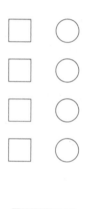

a. There are about 50,000 kinds of spiders.

b. Spiders save the world's food supply by killing insects.

c. Spiders eat mountains and mountains of insects.

d. The human race needs spiders to survive.

Total Comprehension Score
(Add your scores and enter the
total on the graph on page 103.)

Categories of Comprehension Questions

No. 1: Subject Matter	No. 4: Clarifying Devices
No. 2: Supporting Details	No. 5: Vocabulary in Context
No. 3: Conclusion	No. 6: Main Idea

3. Long Fight for a Comeback

Today the whooping crane has a good chance for survival. A few years back, more than fifty whoopers were living at Aransas. This number tells us that the whoopers can win their long fight for a comeback. And the number of cranes is still growing.

Each year around April 15th, the whooping cranes take off for the North. The young born the year before have not yet reached their full height of five feet (about 1.52 meters) and wingspread of seven feet (about 2.1 meters). So far they have lived only with their parents. At Aransas each family stakes out a square mile (about 2.6 square kilometers) for its domain. And woe to the stranger whooper who tries to cross the lines.

It is at this time that the cranes get restless. The males use their long bills to nudge the young. They are hinting that it's time to take off on their own. Meanwhile the male and female rehearse their high-leaping dance of courtship. Then one day a male will fly almost out of sight and circle in the air. It starts calling its loud "Ker-loo! Kerlee-oo!" which sounds like an Indian war whoop. The female and young fly up and circle, too. The family heads north at last.

Within a few days all the whoopers will have left Aransas in families or small groups of unmated birds. They fly high and fast. The trip to Wood Buffalo National Park takes about twenty-two days. The whoopers must come down to feed and rest. When a family arrives in the wild lake country, the young are driven off. Each may join a group of unmated whoopers. Or it may stay alone all summer. It is not yet ready to start its own family.

The female picks a spot in the tall reeds which grow in shallow waters near a lake shore. She builds a three-foot (about .91 meters) platform with its top edge a safe foot (about .31 meters) above the water. Here she lays two speckled, dark green eggs a bit larger than a chicken's. She and her mate take turns keeping them warm. They turn them often so the young will grow well. The eggs hatch in thirty-one days. The chicks are larger and have longer legs than the barnyard kind.

They cheep all day and follow their mother wherever she goes. The male — always on guard against owls, eagles and foxes — stays close by. Both parents feed the chicks from morning till night. With all their care, they are lucky to bring even one chick through its first two weeks. By then it is a foot (about .31 meters) tall. In six weeks its orange down is replaced by brown feathers. It starts to find much of its own food. But it will take all the months ahead, until mid-October, to grow strong flight feathers for the long trip back to the Aransas refuge.

?

	Possible Score	Your Score

1. What would be another good title for this passage?

   ☐ a. Migration and Nesting Habits of the Whooping Cranes
   ☐ b. Whooping Cranes and the Hunting Season
   ☐ c. Has Anyone Seen the Mysterious Cranes?
   ☐ d. Wildlife Refuges for Whooping Cranes

   15   ◯

2. The female crane usually lays

   ☐ a. 1 egg.
   ☐ b. 2 eggs.
   ☐ c. 3 eggs.
   ☐ d. 4 eggs.

   15   ◯

3. We can see that whoopers

   ☐ a. guard their territory carefully.
   ☐ b. sometimes lose their way during migration.
   ☐ c. mostly nest in wheat fields.
   ☐ d. leave their young soon after birth.

   15   ◯

4. The writer compares a crane's egg to a chicken's egg in order to compare their

   ☐ a. color.
   ☐ b. shape.
   ☐ c. size.
   ☐ d. taste.

   15   ◯

5. Another word for restless would be

   ☐ a. uneasy.
   ☐ b. sleepy.
   ☐ c. hungry.
   ☐ d. shy.

   15   ◯

6. Main Idea

	Answer	Score
Mark the main idea	M	(10)
Mark the statement that is a detail	D	(5)
Mark the statement that is too narrow	N	(5)
Mark the statement that is too broad	B	(5)

a. The wingspread of a grown whooping crane is 7 feet (about 1.52 meters).

b. A few years back, more than 50 whoopers were living at Aransas.

c. The whooping crane has been increasing in numbers in recent years.

d. Some birds have come close to disappearing completely.

Total Comprehension Score
(Add your scores and enter the total on the graph on page 103.)

Categories of Comprehension Questions

No. 1: Subject Matter	No. 4: Clarifying Devices
No. 2: Supporting Details	No. 5: Vocabulary in Context
No. 3: Conclusion	No. 6: Main Idea

4. The Landmakers

Mangrove trees do have real fruit. When still on the tree, each fruit sends out a long, thin root. It is now a *seedling*. When the seedling drops from the tree, the root end may stick in the mud and begin to grow.

Once the seedling is rooted, it grows quickly. At the end of the first year, the new mangrove is about two feet (about .61 meters) tall. It is ready to send out its long, stilt-like, prop roots.

The only mangroves north of Mexico are found in the south of Florida and in Hawaii, where it is warm.

Mangrove trees are called *landmakers* for a good reason. The great spreading roots of the red mangrove are like a net. They trap silt, driftwood, leaves, shells, sponges and seaweed. Soon sand or mud builds up around the mangrove trees. The water gets more and more <u>shallow</u>. Then, land appears. In this way beaches are widened. Sometimes an island is formed.

Through the years, many new acres of land are added to the coasts by this steady growth. As the trees keep sprouting at the edge of an island, the island gets larger.

As the shoreline moves out into the water, some of the red mangroves are left inland. These will soon die. The water can no longer wash over the roots of these trees. They need this water to live.

Other kinds of trees which grow well on newly formed land will grow in their place. When living things are replaced by others in this way, the process is called *succession*.

Besides their role in building new land, mangroves help to keep old land from washing away. Mangroves are like fences. They help reduce the force of storm tides that might wash away much of the coastal land.

	Possible Score	Your Score

1. This passage is about

   ☐ a. a type of tree.
   ☐ b. plants of the tropics.
   ☐ c. tropical seeds.
   ☐ d. islands and continents.

   15 ◯

2. In North America mangroves are found in

   ☐ a. Washington and Oregon.
   ☐ b. Nova Scotia and New Brunswick.
   ☐ c. Louisiana and Mississippi.
   ☐ d. Florida and Hawaii.

   15 ◯

3. Mangroves stop

   ☐ a. sleeping sickness.
   ☐ b. soil erosion.
   ☐ c. coral reefs.
   ☐ d. deserts from forming.

   15 ◯

4. A "stilt-like" root is

   ☐ a. soft and moist.
   ☐ b. round and bumpy.
   ☐ c. short and thick.
   ☐ d. long and thin.

   15 ◯

5. Shallow water is

   ☐ a. bottomless.
   ☐ b. very murky.
   ☐ c. not very deep.
   ☐ d. salty.

   15 ◯

6. Main Idea

	Answer	Score
Mark the main idea	M	(10)
Mark the statement that is a detail	D	(5)
Mark the statement that is too narrow	N	(5)
Mark the statement that is too broad	B	(5)

a. Mangroves are fruit trees that build up new land.

b. Some trees can actually be landmakers.

c. Mangroves that are left inland will soon die.

d. The mangrove roots act like a net, trapping silt, leaves and seaweed.

Total Comprehension Score
(Add your scores and enter the
total on the graph on page 103.)

Categories of Comprehension Questions

No. 1: Subject Matter	No. 4: Clarifying Devices
No. 2: Supporting Details	No. 5: Vocabulary in Context
No. 3: Conclusion	No. 6: Main Idea

5. Puffins

Puffins live in colonies. They breed on islands off the Atlantic Coast from Greenland to Maine. At breeding time these birds look as though they stepped right out of a comic book! Their white faces with huge beaks of yellow, blue and reddish-orange sway from side to side. Dressed in their black and white suits, they look like penguins. They waddle along, bolt upright, on big, red, webbed feet.

When a puffin flies, it looks like a fat cigar sailing through the air. As its huge "nose" points the way, its wings beat very fast. It seems to steer with its big feet spread out behind. When fishing, it dives into the sea and dashes about under water. Then it flies out again.

A puffin loves fish. It flies in from the sea with as many as six fish in its bill. It spreads its great webbed feet to land "kerplunk!" It comes down in the middle of a group of its puffin friends. Inside the bird's beak, the fish all face the same direction, heads on one side, tails on the other.

Are you wondering why the first slippery fish doesn't fall out of the puffin's beak when it catches another fish? Well, it is very puzzling. But some experts tell us that they think a puffin holds onto the first fish by clamping it to the roof of its mouth with its tongue. Then it uses the lower part of its beak to go on fishing.

The male and female puffin help each other. They divide the job of getting ready for their chick. Papa Puffin burrows two feet (about .61 meters) or more into a sloping bank. At the end of this short tunnel, he places some dry grass and sometimes a few feathers. On this his mate lays one white egg. Then they take turns warming the egg until it hatches. Each parent completes its turn of keeping the egg warm. Then it comes out of the dark tunnel to stretch its cramped body and flutter its wings.

When the puffin chick is born, its round little body is covered with black <u>down</u> an inch (about 2.5 centimeters) long. It looks just like a black, fluffy powder puff!

	Possible Score	Your Score

1. What would be another good title for this passage?

   ☐ a. Tropical Birds for Sale
   ☐ b. Puffins and Other Game Birds
   ☐ c. Let's Meet the Puffin
   ☐ d. Birds for Pets

   (15) ◯

2. The puffin's diet consists mainly of

   ☐ a. fish.
   ☐ b. rice.
   ☐ c. salt-marsh weeds.
   ☐ d. plants.

   (15) ◯

3. Which of the following is probably true?

   ☐ a. Puffins bear their young alive.
   ☐ b. Puffins leave their eggs to hatch by themselves.
   ☐ c. Young puffins are cared for by both parents.
   ☐ d. Baby puffins are born without feathers.

   (15) ◯

4. In the first paragraph the writer is discussing the puffin's

   ☐ a. mating habits.
   ☐ b. personality.
   ☐ c. eating habits.
   ☐ d. appearance.

   (15) ◯

5. A puffin chick's body is covered with <u>down</u>. Another word for
   down is

   ☐ a. scales.
   ☐ b. feathers.
   ☐ c. spots.
   ☐ d. fur.

   (15) ◯

6. Main Idea

	Answer	Score
Mark the main idea	M	(10)
Mark the statement that is a detail	D	5
Mark the statement that is too narrow	N	5
Mark the statement that is too broad	B	5

a. Puffins are comical-looking, fish-loving birds.

b. Puffins live along the rocky coast of Maine.

c. A puffin can hold as many as 6 fish in its bill at once.

d. Puffins are fishing experts.

Total Comprehension Score
(Add your scores and enter the
total on the graph on page 103.)

Categories of Comprehension Questions

No. 1: Subject Matter	No. 4: Clarifying Devices
No. 2: Supporting Details	No. 5: Vocabulary in Context
No. 3: Conclusion	No. 6: Main Idea

6. Tongues That Do Their Jobs

Giraffe tongues are twenty-one inches (about 53.3 centimeters) long. A giraffe can curl its tongue around leaves and pull the leaves from trees. Okapis (oh CA peez), which look like the giraffes, have such long tongues that they can use them to wash their eyes and ears.

Hummingbirds feed on nectar. They have tongues that are unlike any other creature's. The sides of a hummingbird's tongue curve up and turn in to form a tube! It uses its tongue like a straw, sucking up tiny insects along with the juices of the flower.

Birds like the woodpecker catch their prey with thin, hard-tipped tongues. One type of woodpecker tongue is shaped like a lance. Woodpeckers use it to spear large insects, a favorite kind of food. First, the woodpecker uses its hard bill to find an insect's tunnel in a dead tree. Next, out comes the long tongue — it twists and feels along the tunnel. Then ZAP! it stabs its prey.

Woodpeckers have many fine bristles on the sides of their tongues. These are like the bristles on a brush and are used to lap up tree sap. Certain woodpecker tongues have some parts covered with sticky saliva which traps insects crawling in tree cracks or in anthills.

Other birds have tricky tongues, too. A cockatoo will split a nut with its hooked beak. Then its strong tongue slips in and picks out the meat. Penguins and some other fisheaters have hard spikes on their tongues. They use these to push and guide the slick fish into a swallowing position.

If you have ever been licked by a cat, you have noticed how rough its tongue felt. The center of a cat's tongue is covered with short, fat, pointed bumps. These bumps help cats lick meat off the bones of prey. They also work like the teeth of a comb when they clean themselves. But cats (and dogs, too) need their tongues for one more job. They tell you how much they like you!

Not every animal's tongue may be as long as a giraffe's or as friendly as a cat's, but it does the job it has to do. The next time you see a tongue in action, take a close look at it. Is it licking, sticking, grabbing or stabbing?

?

	Possible Score	Your Score

1. What would be another good title for this passage?

   ☐ a. The Unimportant Uses of the Tongue
   ☐ b. How Tongues Are Used in Grooming
   ☐ c. Some Animals' Tongues in Action
   ☐ d. Some Animals Use Their Tongues To Smell

   Possible Score: 15   **Your Score:** ◯

2. Hummingbirds feed on

   ☐ a. nectar.
   ☐ b. large insects.
   ☐ c. tree sap.
   ☐ d. leaves.

   Possible Score: 15   **Your Score:** ◯

3. The woodpecker is a

   ☐ a. dog.
   ☐ b. snake.
   ☐ c. frog.
   ☐ d. bird.

   Possible Score: 15   **Your Score:** ◯

4. When a cat or dog uses its tongue to lick, it is being

   ☐ a. shy.
   ☐ b. nervous.
   ☐ c. friendly.
   ☐ d. quarrelsome.

   Possible Score: 15   **Your Score:** ◯

5. Bristles are

   ☐ a. small, velvety bumps.
   ☐ b. short, stiff hairs.
   ☐ c. knifelike edges.
   ☐ d. tubelike tongues.

   Possible Score: 15   **Your Score:** ◯

6. Main Idea

	Answer	Score
Mark the main idea	M	⑩
Mark the statement that is a detail	D	⑤
Mark the statement that is too narrow	N	⑤
Mark the statement that is too broad	B	⑤

a. The tongues of animals have special jobs to do.

b. The tongues of animals are all different.

c. Some woodpeckers have sticky tongues.

d. The tongues of some animals can tell us how much they like us.

Total Comprehension Score
(Add your scores and enter the
total on the graph on page 103.)

Categories of Comprehension Questions

No. 1: Subject Matter	No. 4: Clarifying Devices
No. 2: Supporting Details	No. 5: Vocabulary in Context
No. 3: Conclusion	No. 6: Main Idea

7. Food For Thought

Grass covers nearly one-fourth of the whole earth. It provides food for people and animals. It protects hilly <u>pastures</u> from washing away. It carpets our lawns and parks. In Asia a giant grass, bamboo, is used to build houses, to make tools, bowls and even paper.

Much of the food we eat comes from grass. Bread is made from flour, which is made by grinding the seeds of grasses. The seeds of wheat and rye are the most common grains used to make bread. Corn, rice, oats, barley and millet are other grasses whose seeds are made into bread and cereals. Much of the sugar that sweetens our desserts was refined from stem juices of a giant grass, sugarcane.

Many of the world's other animals eat grass, too. Cattle, sheep, goats and many wild animals live mostly on grass. They change this green grass into meat and milk, which people eat. Many meat-eating animals eat grass-eating animals; so their food, too, comes first from grass.

There are over 6,000 different kinds, or varieties, of grass in this huge plant family. Some of the grasses are tiny, hairlike, green strands. Others, like the giant bamboos, are as tall as trees.

Some grasses, such as corn and sugarcane, have stems filled with a soft material. This is the part of the sugarcane that has the sweet juice from which sugar is made.

Some grasses grow from seeds each year. They come up in the spring, grow, bloom, make seeds and die. These are called *annual,* or yearly, grasses. Other grass plants live from one year to the next. Each spring they send up new stems and leaves from the same roots. These are the *perennial,* or many-year, grasses.

Life on earth would be much poorer without the grasses, for these green stems and leaves and nutritious seeds feed so many people and animals.

?

	Possible Score	Your Score

1. This passage is mostly about grass and

   ☐ a. its uses.
   ☐ b. how to grow it.
   ☐ c. landscaping.
   ☐ d. its history.

   15   ◯

2. How many kinds of grasses are there?

   ☐ a. 75
   ☐ b. 150
   ☐ c. 1,000
   ☐ d. Over 6,000

   15   ◯

3. This passage leads us to believe that grasses are an important part of

   ☐ a. farming.
   ☐ b. our food supply.
   ☐ c. our oceans.
   ☐ d. a greenhouse.

   15   ◯

4. The writer feels that grass is

   ☐ a. grown in few places.
   ☐ b. valuable.
   ☐ c. unnecessary.
   ☐ d. hard to take care of.

   15   ◯

5. Pastures are

   ☐ a. large, polluted lakes.
   ☐ b. small, swampy places.
   ☐ c. rapid, flowing rivers.
   ☐ d. areas used for grazing.

   15   ◯

6. Main Idea

	Answer	Score
Mark the main idea	M	(10)
Mark the statement that is a detail	D	5
Mark the statement that is too narrow	N	5
Mark the statement that is too broad	B	5

a. Bamboo is a giant grass. ☐ ◯

b. The seeds of wheat and rye supply much food. ☐ ◯

c. Grass is more important than many people think. ☐ ◯

d. Much of the food we eat comes from grass. ☐ ◯

Total Comprehension Score
(Add your scores and enter the
total on the graph on page 103.)

Categories of Comprehension Questions

No. 1: Subject Matter	No. 4: Clarifying Devices
No. 2: Supporting Details	No. 5: Vocabulary in Context
No. 3: Conclusion	No. 6: Main Idea

8. The Largest Animal on Earth

Take a guess. What is the largest kind of animal that has ever lived on earth? If you guess "a dinosaur," you are mistaken.

The largest animal ever to live on earth is living now. It is a kind of whale — the blue whale. A fully grown female can be 100 feet (about 30.5 meters) long. That is as long as six station wagons parked bumper to bumper!

That's not all! The adult female can also weigh 120 to 150 tons (about 108 to 135 tonnes). That's as much as 80 to 100 small cars.

What about the second-largest animal? Would you have guessed a dinosaur? You would have been wrong again. It's another kind of whale — the fin whale. Adult fin whales are about 79 feet (about 23.7 meters) long and weigh up to 70 tons (about 63 tonnes). What about the *third* largest? the fourth? the fifth? the sixth? You're right if you say — more whales.

Perhaps you are thinking to yourself, "Those whales are mighty big fish." Whales are not fish. A whale is a *mammal* — just as a cow, a cat, a beaver, a seal or a human is a mammal.

Baby whales are fed on mother's milk, just like all mammal babies on land. Baby fish do not need milk, and adult fish do not make any.

Though they get their food underwater, whales must come above the surface to breathe air just as human swimmers do. A fish does not breathe air — it takes oxygen from the water passing through its gills.

Have you ever watched dolphins on a TV show? Playful, aren't they? Dolphins are small whales. Large whales play too. Humpback whales that weigh 50 tons (about 45 tonnes) can leap high into the air, do a back-flip and crash into the water again.

Some kinds of whales seem to make close, loving friends with each other. The sixty-six-foot (about 19.8-meter) sperm whales "stand up" in the water and hug each other with their flippers. So do humpback whales.

Some whales sing. The songs of humpback whales have been recorded. They are something like birds' songs, only much longer, and with both higher and lower notes. Each humpback whale ends a song with a sound all its own, a sort of *signature.*

45

?

	Possible Score	Your Score

1. This passage is mostly about

   ☐ a. how whales sing.
   ☐ b. baby whales.
   ☐ c. the size of whales.
   ☐ d. dolphins on TV.

   ⑮ ◯

2. A whale is a

   ☐ a. reptile.
   ☐ b. fish.
   ☐ c. amphibian.
   ☐ d. mammal.

   ⑮ ◯

3. Whales do not have

   ☐ a. a voice.
   ☐ b. gills.
   ☐ c. flippers.
   ☐ d. teeth.

   ⑮ ◯

4. The writer compares the weight of the blue whale to the weight of

   ☐ a. 6 station wagons.
   ☐ b. the fin whale.
   ☐ c. several dinosaurs.
   ☐ d. 80–100 cars.

   ⑮ ◯

5. As used in this passage, <u>leap</u> means to

   ☐ a. fall down.
   ☐ b. jump.
   ☐ c. swim.
   ☐ d. crash into.

   ⑮ ◯

6. Main Idea

	Answer	Score
Mark the main idea	M	(10)
Mark the statement that is a detail	D	(5)
Mark the statement that is too narrow	N	(5)
Mark the statement that is too broad	B	(5)

a. Whales, the largest animals, live in the sea, but aren't fish.

b. There's more to a whale than its size.

c. Whales must come above the water surface to breathe.

d. The playful dolphins seen on TV shows are whales.

Total Comprehension Score
(Add your scores and enter the
total on the graph on page 103.)

Categories of Comprehension Questions

No. 1: Subject Matter	No. 4: Clarifying Devices
No. 2: Supporting Details	No. 5: Vocabulary in Context
No. 3: Conclusion	No. 6: Main Idea

9. The Ancient Dragonfly

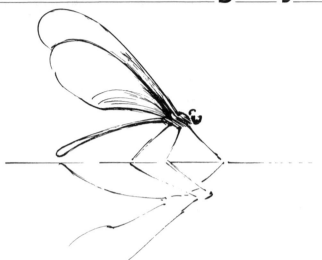

Millions of years before there were dinosaurs, huge dragonflies flew through the swamps. They were the largest insects ever to have lived on earth. Some dragonflies were about thirty inches (about 76.2 centimeters) across from wing to wing. Some had a body about twelve inches (about 30.5 centimeters) long.

Today's dragonflies are much smaller. But they still look a lot like those big dragons of the past. Dragonflies have not changed much in the last 300 million years.

But an insect can be "old-fashioned" and still get along fine today. The dragonfly is an acrobat in the air. It can fly fast — almost thirty-one miles (about 49.9 kilometers) per hour.

If you watch a dragonfly near a pond or stream, you may see it dart back and forth over the same stretch of water. When it rests, it goes to the same perch. It likes to perch on a plant or log in the water. This is a male dragonfly. He is guarding his kingdom — his own part of the water. If another male dragonfly flies into the male's kingdom, the two males fight.

When a female dragonfly comes into the male's kingdom, he <u>courts</u> her and mates with her. She lays her eggs in his part of the water.

The little creature that hatches from the egg in the water is called a *nymph* (nimf). The nymph stays in the water for one to five years. As it grows, it sheds its hard outside shell about twelve times — which we call *molting*. Under the old shell is a new, soft shell. The new shell grows a bit and then turns hard. When this hard shell gets too small, the insect molts once more.

The nymph molts many times. Then one day it crawls out of the water onto a branch, a plant stem or up on the shore. Here it will molt for the last time. It then carries on the rest of its life as an adult.

	Possible Score	Your Score

1. Dragonflies are

   ☐ a. insects.
   ☐ b. reptiles.
   ☐ c. mammals.
   ☐ d. plants.

   (15) ◯

2. Where do dragonflies live?

   ☐ a. In plants in the garden
   ☐ b. Near ponds or streams
   ☐ c. Underground
   ☐ d. In trees

   (15) ◯

3. The next to last paragraph suggests that it takes a long time for a dragonfly

   ☐ a. to find enough food.
   ☐ b. to mate.
   ☐ c. to become an adult.
   ☐ d. to find a home.

   (15) ◯

4. When a male dragonfly guards his kingdom, he is

   ☐ a. inviting other dragonflies to enter.
   ☐ b. keeping trespassers out.
   ☐ c. trying to find a new home.
   ☐ d. looking for food.

   (15) ◯

5. When a male dragonfly courts a female, he is trying to

   ☐ a. attract her.
   ☐ b. kill her.
   ☐ c. drive her away.
   ☐ d. fight with her.

   (15) ◯

6. Main Idea

	Answer	Score
Mark the main idea	M	(10)
Mark the statement that is a detail	D	(5)
Mark the statement that is too narrow	N	(5)
Mark the statement that is too broad	B	(5)

a. Dragonflies can be called "old-fashioned."

b. Their only change has been to a slightly smaller size.

c. Ancient dragonflies were about 30 inches (about 76.2 centimeters) across from wing to wing.

d. Dragonflies have not changed much in the last 300 million years.

Total Comprehension Score
(Add your scores and enter the
total on the graph on page 103.)

Categories of Comprehension Questions

No. 1: Subject Matter	No. 4: Clarifying Devices
No. 2: Supporting Details	No. 5: Vocabulary in Context
No. 3: Conclusion	No. 6: Main Idea

10. Rodents

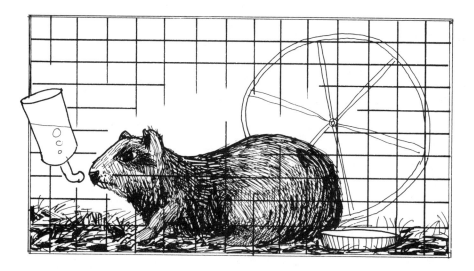

Though they are unlike in many ways, all rodents, such as mice, beaver and squirrels, do have one thing in common. If you could look them full in the face, you would find that they all have four large, chisel-shaped front teeth — two up and two down. In fact, the word "rodent" comes from an old Latin word that means "to gnaw" or "to chew."

The rodent's front teeth do all kinds of jobs. Some rodents use them to cut wood for food. Some use them to cut wood to build homes. The gnawing, gnawing, gnawing wears down their teeth.

But the teeth keep on growing — just as your hair and nails do. This steady growth could get the rodents in trouble. The teeth could keep growing until the bottom teeth grow up in front of the nose. The top teeth could curl up and grow through the roof of the mouth. So when they can't find lots of hard food, rodents must grind their teeth together to keep them worn down.

Each kind of rodent has its own story. The rich coat of the beaver, for instance, was hunted by early trappers. The fur of this dam-builder caused the trappers to move north and west into the North American wilds and explore new regions.

Gerbils (JUR bills) are those small, friendly rodents that look a bit like tiny kangaroos. They come from the deserts of Africa and Asia. There they burrow in the sand. They dare to come out only at night and hop around like big grasshoppers.

The most common kind of hamster is the golden hamster. Years ago, a litter of these rodents was caught in North Africa. These babies were taken to Israel. There they grew up and had young of their own. Through the years more babies were born. The hamsters became so popular as pets that they were shipped all over the world.

?

	Possible Score	Your Score

1. This passage is mostly about

    ☐ a. the mating habits of the rodent family.
    ☐ b. what is different and what is the same about rodents.
    ☐ c. the germs and sicknesses that rodents carry.   **(15)**   ◯
    ☐ d. the history of rats and mice.

2. The word "rodent" means

    ☐ a. to gnaw.
    ☐ b. milk.
    ☐ c. small eyes.   **(15)**   ◯
    ☐ d. sly.

3. Some rodents

    ☐ a. make good pets.
    ☐ b. have no teeth.
    ☐ c. dislike water.   **(15)**   ◯
    ☐ d. have never been seen by human beings.

4. Early trappers could also be called

    ☐ a. soldiers.
    ☐ b. explorers.
    ☐ c. ministers.   **(15)**   ◯
    ☐ d. inventors.

5. As used in this passage, <u>burrow</u> means to

    ☐ a. hop.
    ☐ b. lie down.
    ☐ c. dig.   **(15)**   ◯
    ☐ d. play.

6. Main Idea

	Answer	Score
Mark the main idea	M	⑩
Mark the statement that is a detail	D	⑤
Mark the statement that is too narrow	N	⑤
Mark the statement that is too broad	B	⑤

a. There are many different kinds of rodents, but all have four sharp front teeth.

b. Gerbils look like tiny kangaroos.

c. Rodents have to gnaw to wear down their teeth.

d. Sharp teeth are very important to some animals.

Total Comprehension Score
(Add your scores and enter the total on the graph on page 103.)

Categories of Comprehension Questions

No. 1: Subject Matter	No. 4: Clarifying Devices
No. 2: Supporting Details	No. 5: Vocabulary in Context
No. 3: Conclusion	No. 6: Main Idea

11. Squirrel Watching

As I watched the flying squirrels dart about, I learned many things. I saw them search for moths and other insects for food. Sometimes they would feed on seeds and buds of trees.

I have found out that I am not the only one who enjoys these furry creatures. Some people living nearby are trying to attract them to their homes. They place fruit, nuts or seeds near the woods. Each night the people move the food closer to their houses. The squirrels get used to the yard lights. Soon the people watch the squirrels from inside the house or even from outside.

Most often April and May are the times when young squirrels are born. But they may be born at all times during the summer, even early fall. The mother is devoted to her young. She will risk her life in their defense.

One day I noticed some people sawing off a <u>limb</u> of a tree which stood near a river. They soon found that a flying squirrel had built her nest there. But it was too late — the nest had been damaged. One of the men pulled four hairless babies from the nest. As he held them, not knowing what to do, the mother squirrel climbed up his pant leg.

She grasped one baby in her mouth and ran down to the ground. Then she took it to the top of another tree. She sailed with her baby eighty-six feet (about 26.2 meters) across the river and carried it up to a hole in another tree. She made more trips until all her young were safe in their new home. Flying squirrels are amazing little animals!

?

1. What would be another good title for this passage?

   ☐ a. Mating of the Flying Squirrel
   ☐ b. Do They Really Fly?
   ☐ c. What to Do When You Meet a Squirrel
   ☐ d. A Daring Rescue

   Possible Score (15) Your Score ◯

2. Young squirrels are born in

   ☐ a. April and May.
   ☐ b. June and July.
   ☐ c. August and September.
   ☐ d. October and November.

   Possible Score (15) Your Score ◯

3. In certain situations a female squirrel can be very

   ☐ a. selfish.
   ☐ b. fearless.
   ☐ c. foolish.
   ☐ d. romantic.

   Possible Score (15) Your Score ◯

4. The mother squirrel felt that her babies

   ☐ a. were lost forever.
   ☐ b. were too much trouble.
   ☐ c. could take care of themselves.
   ☐ d. were in danger.

   Possible Score (15) Your Score ◯

5. The limb of a tree refers to its

   ☐ a. leaves.
   ☐ b. branches.
   ☐ c. roots.
   ☐ d. trunk.

   Possible Score (15) Your Score ◯

6. Main Idea

	Answer	Score
Mark the main idea	M	(10)
Mark the statement that is a detail	D	(5)
Mark the statement that is too narrow	N	(5)
Mark the statement that is too broad	B	(5)

a. Some animals interest people more than others.

b. Flying squirrels can glide through the air as far as 80–90 feet (about 24–27 meters).

c. Some people try to attract the squirrels to their homes.

d. The flying squirrel attracts much attention by its daily actions.

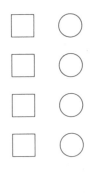

Total Comprehension Score
(Add your scores and enter the
total on the graph on page 103.)

Categories of Comprehension Questions

No. 1: Subject Matter	No. 4: Clarifying Devices
No. 2: Supporting Details	No. 5: Vocabulary in Context
No. 3: Conclusion	No. 6: Main Idea

12. Snowshoes

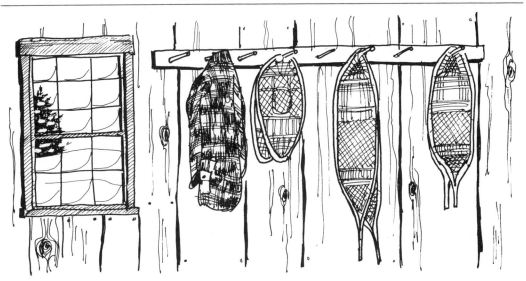

Finding your method of snow travel will depend on your type of ground. Snowshoes are best on deep snow, in hilly country or in dense brush. Skis do best on clean, flat country and in cold, dry snow. Snowshoes are slow and steady. Skis are great on flat ground or downhill, but harder to climb with.

In picking a pair of snowshoes, care should be taken not only to get a good pair, but also to get the right design. There are many styles, and each has its virtues. *Bear paws* are oval-shaped shoes with no tail. They are good for hilly country or going through thick brush. Since they are short and tailless, they can be turned sharply and easily. But, to make up for their shortness, they are quite wide. Therefore, they are hard for a beginner to use. *Pickerel snowshoes* are long and narrow with sharply turned-up toes. They are good for going long distances in the open lake country or above the tree line in the mountains. But their length makes them a headache if you're trying to thread your way through dense cover. For all-around use and for the beginner, the best choice is a shoe between these two extremes. Sometimes called a *trail shoe,* this one is shaped like a teardrop. It is about one foot (about .31 meters) across at the widest part and about four feet (about 12.2 meters) long. It has a tail, and the toe is slightly turned up to keep it from digging in and piling up with snow. United States makers build these with a round toe. The ones from Canada are pointed. No one knows why, but no matter — both are good, all-around shoes.

The most important thing to check when you get a pair of snowshoes is the balance. There must be enough weight *behind* the turning point of your bindings. If there isn't, the tail of your shoe may lift when you pick up your foot. This lets the toe dig in or "dive." Digging in a toe causes you to pitch on your face in the snow. But, with the right bindings and a balanced pair of shoes, it is no problem.

	Possible Score	Your Score

1. This passage is mostly about snowshoes and

   ☐ a. how they are made.
   ☐ b. their different styles.
   ☐ c. who first used them.
   ☐ d. their main disadvantages.   (15)   ◯

2. Snowshoes that are long and narrow with turned-up toes are called

   ☐ a. banana shoes.
   ☐ b. pickerel snowshoes.
   ☐ c. trail shoes.
   ☐ d. pivot snowshoes.   (15)   ◯

3. Which of the following is most likely true?

   ☐ a. Most mountain people make their own snowshoes.
   ☐ b. Some snowshoes are made of aluminum.
   ☐ c. Using snowshoes requires a little practice.
   ☐ d. The balance of a snowshoe is not important.   (15)   ◯

4. The last paragraph discusses the

   ☐ a. length of the snowshoes.
   ☐ b. weight of the snowshoes.
   ☐ c. advantages of snowshoes.
   ☐ d. balance of the snowshoes.   (15)   ◯

5. Each style has its own virtues. As used in this sentence, *virtues* refers to the

   ☐ a. good points of a snowshoe.
   ☐ b. materials used in snowshoes.
   ☐ c. disadvantages of snowshoes.
   ☐ d. kind of people using snowshoes.   (15)   ◯

6. Main Idea

	Answer	Score
Mark the main idea	M	⑩
Mark the statement that is a detail	D	⑤
Mark the statement that is too narrow	N	⑤
Mark the statement that is too broad	B	⑤

a. The snowshoes made in Canada are pointed.

b. Snowshoes make it easier to travel in the snow.

c. Picking a snowshoe depends on where you want to wear it.

d. Oval-shaped snowshoes are good for hilly country.

Total Comprehension Score
(Add your scores and enter the
total on the graph on page 103.)

Categories of Comprehension Questions

No. 1: Subject Matter	No. 4: Clarifying Devices
No. 2: Supporting Details	No. 5: Vocabulary in Context
No. 3: Conclusion	No. 6: Main Idea

13. Mini Fruit Trees

Don't throw away the seeds from oranges, tangerines, lemons or grapefruit. Instead, soak them in water for about twelve hours. Then plant them about one inch (about 2.5 centimeters) deep in flowerpots or cut-down milk cartons with holes punched in the bottom. These holes will allow extra water to drain off. Use garden soil mixed with some <u>coarse</u> sand and a handful of peat moss. In the city you can buy soil in small bags at dime stores and some grocery stores. Plant two or three seeds in each pot.

Put the pots in a sunny window and water them well every few days. Use liquid plant food each month or six weeks. (You can buy this where you buy the soil.) Turn the pots often so the plants will grow straight. If you don't turn them, the plants will lean toward the sun.

Seeds of other fruits, such as apples and pears, will also grow. Put them between a few layers of paper towels in a baking pan. Then pour water on them so they are soaked. Keep the pan in a dark, warm spot for about a month. Be sure the towels are wet all through this time.

When you open the towels, some of the seeds will have sprouted. Gently put the sprouts into a pot of soil and water well. Keep in a sunny window. In no time you will have an orchard of tiny fruit trees.

?

	Possible Score	Your Score

1. What would be another good title for this passage?

   ☐ a. Fruit Trees and Greenhouses
   ☐ b. How to Make Flowerpots
   ☐ c. Why Some Seeds Don't Grow
   ☐ d. An Orchard From Household Fruits

   Possible Score: **15**   Your Score: ◯

2. Liquid plant food should be used every

   ☐ a. week.
   ☐ b. month.
   ☐ c. 6 months.
   ☐ d. 8 months.

   Possible Score: **15**   Your Score: ◯

3. Two or three seeds should be planted together because

   ☐ a. not every seed will sprout.
   ☐ b. the extra seeds will soak up unneeded water.
   ☐ c. the other seeds provide food for the sprouting plant.
   ☐ d. it takes more than one seed to make a root system.

   Possible Score: **15**   Your Score: ◯

4. Plant nutrients can be compared to

   ☐ a. weed killer.
   ☐ b. vitamins.
   ☐ c. candy.
   ☐ d. soap.

   Possible Score: **15**   Your Score: ◯

5. Coarse sand is made of

   ☐ a. large grains of sand.
   ☐ b. peat moss.
   ☐ c. rocks and sand.
   ☐ d. vegetable matter.

   Possible Score: **15**   Your Score: ◯

6. Main Idea

	Answer	Score
Mark the main idea	M	(10)
Mark the statement that is a detail	D	(5)
Mark the statement that is too narrow	N	(5)
Mark the statement that is too broad	B	(5)

a. People can grow their own fruit trees. ☐ ◯

b. Fruit trees can be grown at home from seeds. ☐ ◯

c. An orange tree can be grown at home from seeds. ☐ ◯

d. All sides of the pot must get equal sun for the plant to grow straight. ☐ ◯

Total Comprehension Score
(Add your scores and enter the
total on the graph on page 103.)

Categories of Comprehension Questions

No. 1: Subject Matter	No. 4: Clarifying Devices
No. 2: Supporting Details	No. 5: Vocabulary in Context
No. 3: Conclusion	No. 6: Main Idea

14. The Spider With the Trap Door

The female trap-door spider builds a door of earth to cover her burrow. Next she weaves a hinge on one side of her door. Then she pulls the door down.

The spider builds up the sides of her burrow to fit the outline of the door. It is always an exact fit. If the ground on top has grass, she puts bits of grass or weeds on the top of the door. They may take root and hide the door from the keenest eyes.

Now her joint home and trap are done. She settles down just beneath the door to wait for a passing meal. When she senses the vibrations of an insect above, she flips the door up, reaches out and grabs the victim.

She must not come all the way out of the burrow though. She always leaves her back legs hooked in two holes on the bottom side of the door to keep it from dropping shut for two reasons. The door fits so <u>snugly</u> that even she would have a hard time getting it open again. The other reason is that her eyes are right on top of her head. She can't see downward. She might not be able to find her door again!

Little is known about the male trap-door spider. How he comes and goes is a mystery.

Mating of the spiders is also a mystery. The female will let nothing enter her home, not even a male spider. It is believed that they meet at her front door to mate. Her eggs are laid at the bottom of her burrow. As soon as they hatch, she shoves the babies out. If the eggs are not fertile, she eats them.

She has one enemy — the spider wasp. If one gets near her door, and the spider is careless enough to open the door to grab it, she is stung. The wasp then drags her into its own burrow and lays eggs on her body. When these eggs hatch, the tiny wasp larvae eat the remains of the spider's body. The trap-door spider needs a sign on the underside of her door: "Look before you grab!"

?

	Possible Score	Your Score

1. This passage is mostly about the trap-door spider and how it

   ☐ a. lives.
   ☐ b. raises its young.
   ☐ c. spins a web.
   ☐ d. finds water.

   (15)   ◯

2. What does the spider do with eggs that are not fertile?

   ☐ a. She sits on them.
   ☐ b. She throws them away.
   ☐ c. She buries them.
   ☐ d. She eats them.

   (15)   ◯

3. The spider wasp uses the trap-door spider as

   ☐ a. bait for other insects.
   ☐ b. part of its nest.
   ☐ c. food for its young.
   ☐ d. a way of getting underground.

   (15)   ◯

4. In this passage which of the following is used to hide the trap-door?

   ☐ a. Rivers and ponds
   ☐ b. Bits of grass and weeds
   ☐ c. A fur covering
   ☐ d. Thick green cloth

   (15)   ◯

5. The door fits <u>snugly.</u> This means the door fits

   ☐ a. clumsily.
   ☐ b. tightly.
   ☐ c. loosely.
   ☐ d. awkwardly.

   (15)   ◯

6. Main Idea

	Answer	Score
Mark the main idea	M	(10)
Mark the statement that is a detail	D	(5)
Mark the statement that is too narrow	N	(5)
Mark the statement that is too broad	B	(5)

a. The trap-door spider can sense slight vibrations.

b. Some spiders hunt with trap doors.

c. The trap-door spider is a clever builder and hunter.

d. The trap-door spider places bits of grass to hide its door.

Total Comprehension Score
(Add your scores and enter the total on the graph on page 103.)

Categories of Comprehension Questions

No. 1: Subject Matter	No. 4: Clarifying Devices
No. 2: Supporting Details	No. 5: Vocabulary in Context
No. 3: Conclusion	No. 6: Main Idea

15. Good Eating, But Watch Out!

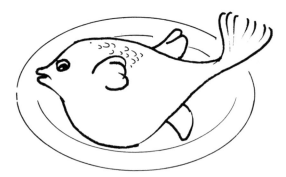

The sea is filled with the wonders of nature. One of the strangest is the puffer fish. Puffers feed on worms, mollusks and shrimp. They eat shellfish which they crunch with their hard jaws. A crab is likely to nip if attacked. Puffers often team up and work with each other to tackle a crab.

North American puffers live in low water near the shore in the summer. They move to deeper water in winter. From Cape Cod to Florida, they dig into sandy shores in May and June to lay their tiny eggs. The babies look like yellow, orange, red or black dots.

Many people in Canada and the United States will not eat cooked puffer (sometimes known as *sea-squab*) because some parts are poison to humans. But in Japan cooked puffer (*fugu*) is thought of as a treat. Yet few cooks know how to make it. The secret is this: on each side of a puffer is a small *fillet* of white flesh. This piece of fish without bones must be neatly removed. The rest of the fish is <u>discarded</u>. The fillet is the only part that can be cooked to eat.

In Japan people dry and stretch puffer skins. Then they put candles in them. The skins glow as if they were made of oiled paper. In the South Seas, natives make fancy helmets from dried puffer skins.

A puffer may nip at your feet when you go swimming at the beach, but it will not really hurt you. Most often puffers will swell up as soon as you take them out of the water. If you catch one that doesn't, just tickle it on the tummy. It won't giggle, but it will do its magic trick of flowing up into a big round ball.

	Possible Score	Your Score

1. This passage is mostly about

    ☐ a. the many kinds of puffer fish.
    ☐ b. the habits and uses of the puffer.
    ☐ c. the mating habits of puffers.   **(15)**   ◯
    ☐ d. the dangerous puffer fish.

2. Many people will not eat cooked puffer because

    ☐ a. it has a bitter taste.
    ☐ b. it is tough.
    ☐ c. it has many bones.   **(15)**   ◯
    ☐ d. parts of it are poisonous.

3. The skin of the puffer seems to be

    ☐ a. delicate.
    ☐ b. dark-colored.
    ☐ c. tough.   **(15)**   ◯
    ☐ d. light-colored.

4. In Japan cooked puffer is a special treat. This means it is

    ☐ a. not served often.
    ☐ b. part of a main dish.
    ☐ c. not good to eat.   **(15)**   ◯
    ☐ d. poisonous.

5. A discarded fish has been

    ☐ a. eaten.
    ☐ b. thrown out.
    ☐ c. cooked.   **(15)**   ◯
    ☐ d. cleaned.

6. Main Idea

	Answer	Score
Mark the main idea	M	(10)
Mark the statement that is a detail	D	5
Mark the statement that is too narrow	N	5
Mark the statement that is too broad	B	5

a. The puffer fish tastes good, but some parts are poisonous.

b. The puffer is an unusual fish that some people find useful and tasty, but that others are happiest to leave in the sea.

c. In Japan cooked puffer is thought of as a treat.

d. The puffer fish is one that you must be very careful with.

Total Comprehension Score
(Add your scores and enter the total on the graph on page 103.)

Categories of Comprehension Questions

No. 1: Subject Matter	No. 4: Clarifying Devices
No. 2: Supporting Details	No. 5: Vocabulary in Context
No. 3: Conclusion	No. 6: Main Idea

16. Rap-Rap-Rap

Lots of people have seen at least one kind of woodpecker because woodpeckers live all over the world. There are more than twenty kinds in North America. They live where there are trees or even large cacti.

You can look for a bird with bright red or yellow on its head. But better yet, *listen* for one. You can't miss its loud *rap-rap-rap* on the side of a hollow tree.

To make its <u>famous</u> sound, the woodpecker has some special tools. In order to hammer hard, a woodpecker uses its stiff tail to brace itself. To hammer without a brace would be like swinging a baseball bat while you are standing on one foot.

A woodpecker's feet are built to hang onto the sides of trees. Most birds have three toes that point frontwards and one that points back. A woodpecker has two toes pointing frontwards and two pointing back.

Its beak is a hard, sharp chisel. Its skull is as solid as concrete, so it's shockproof.

All woodpeckers use their sharp beaks to chisel nest holes. Some use them for chipping away pieces of bark to find insects hidden underneath. And some use their beaks for catching grubs that burrow deep inside trees.

It's fun to watch one of these woodpeckers at work. First, it listens for a grub chewing a tunnel through the wood. Then it starts chopping a hole. It aims first in one direction, then the other, just as a person does with a hatchet. After a few minutes the woodpecker's hole may meet the grub's tunnel.

Then the woodpecker puts its long tongue to work. It snakes its tongue along the grub's tunnel and, with the pointed tip, spears the juicy insect. The woodpecker then pulls its tongue back, and the tasty treat comes with it. What a way to dine!

	Possible Score	Your Score

1. This passage is about

☐ a. North American birds.
☐ b. woodpeckers.
☐ c. young woodpeckers.
☐ d. hummingbirds.

(15)   ◯

2. Some woodpeckers make holes in trees to get

☐ a. water.
☐ b. bark.
☐ c. food.
☐ d. the pulp.

(15)   ◯

3. From this passage we can see that

☐ a. woodpeckers are built for hammering.
☐ b. some birds catch fish.
☐ c. grubs are poisonous to birds.
☐ d. woodpeckers are few in number.

(15)   ◯

4. The writer feels that watching a woodpecker at work is

☐ a. a waste of time.
☐ b. difficult.
☐ c. a good hobby.
☐ d. fun.

(15)   ◯

5. The woodpecker's <u>famous</u> sound is

☐ a. ear-piercing.
☐ b. very rare.
☐ c. well known.
☐ d. soft and low.

(15)   ◯

6. Main Idea

	Answer	Score
Mark the main idea	M	(10)
Mark the statement that is a detail	D	5
Mark the statement that is too narrow	N	5
Mark the statement that is too broad	B	5

a. Nature has been very kind to the woodpecker.

b. The skull of a woodpecker is as solid as concrete.

c. There are more than 20 kinds of woodpeckers in North America.

d. Woodpeckers have wonderful tools.

Total Comprehension Score
(Add your scores and enter the
total on the graph on page 103.)

Categories of Comprehension Questions

No. 1: Subject Matter	No. 4: Clarifying Devices
No. 2: Supporting Details	No. 5: Vocabulary in Context
No. 3: Conclusion	No. 6: Main Idea

17. There's No Place Like Home!

If you were to take a walk by the seashore, you might not see a small limpet clinging to a rock. It could be as small as your little fingernail. But some limpets can be almost an inch (about 2.5 centimeters) in circumference. A limpet's shell is shaped like a pointed straw hat.

Often, when the tide is high, the limpet will leave its place on the rocks to search for food. It slowly glides along, using its flat, strong foot. It won't go far, usually just a few inches (about several centimeters), two or three feet (about .61 or .91 meters) at most.

What does the limpet like to eat? It dines on seaweed now and then. Mostly it likes to eat the tender algae that covers stones and boulders with slick green film. A limpet's tongue is called a *radula* (RAJ oo luh). It is well built for scraping the places where algae grow. Its tongue looks like a file and is made up of tiny teeth.

As the tide begins to fall, the limpet stops eating and goes back home. It will follow the path that it took on its way out. When the limpet reaches the place where it lives, it won't settle down to rest until it has found the special spot that belongs to it. This place has marks and grooves that fit only it, and no other limpet.

The limpet feels about carefully with its foot as if to be sure it is in the right place. Then it lowers its shell and twists it. The shell fits tightly against the rock. This keeps the limpet from drying out when the tide is out. It is also safe from foes and rough surf.

In California some scientists did experiments with some of these creatures. They marked some limpets with paint and put a matching number on the spot where each lived. The limpets moved away to feed, then came right back to the spots marked with the matching numbers. There's no place like home to a limpet!

	Possible Score	Your Score

1. This passage is mostly about the limpet and its

  ☐ a. neighbor the clam.
  ☐ b. shell.
  ☐ c. eating habits.
  ☐ d. young.

  (15) ◯

2. The limpet feeds mostly on

  ☐ a. animals.
  ☐ b. non-green plants.
  ☐ c. insects.
  ☐ d. algae.

  (15) ◯

3. The limpet searches for food

  ☐ a. when the tide is low.
  ☐ b. at night.
  ☐ c. at high tide.
  ☐ d. early in the morning.

  (15) ◯

4. The writer mentions the experiments with limpets to show

  ☐ a. that they always return to the same spot.
  ☐ b. how they give birth.
  ☐ c. the natural enemies of the limpet.
  ☐ d. how some limpets can easily dry out.

  (15) ◯

5. Boulders are

  ☐ a. very large stones.
  ☐ b. pieces of driftwood.
  ☐ c. abandoned shells.
  ☐ d. small, underground caves.

  (15) ◯

6. Main Idea

	Answer	Score
Mark the main idea	M	⑩
Mark the statement that is a detail	D	⑤
Mark the statement that is too narrow	N	⑤
Mark the statement that is too broad	B	⑤

a. Limpets appear to be creatures of strong habit.

b. The limpet eats out, but always returns to its own special spot.

c. A limpet's tongue, like a file, is made up of tiny teeth.

d. A limpet twists its shell onto its special rock.

Total Comprehension Score
(Add your scores and enter the total on the graph on page 103.)

Categories of Comprehension Questions

No. 1: Subject Matter	No. 4: Clarifying Devices
No. 2: Supporting Details	No. 5: Vocabulary in Context
No. 3: Conclusion	No. 6: Main Idea

74

18. Woody Woodchuck

Have you ever seen a male woodchuck? He is that small, brown animal, also called a ground hog, that is always popping up in the middle of the farmer's green field.

Woody is born early in the spring in a burrow under the ground. He is very tiny and has no hair, but his mother has made a warm nest of grass for him. Usually he has three or four brothers and sisters. His mother nurses him just the way a mother cat nurses her kittens. After three or four weeks, his mother brings him some <u>greens</u> to eat. Soon his eyes open, and Woody can go out of the burrow to get his own greens.

His mother watches him closely when he goes out. Often her shrill "danger" whistle sends him running and tumbling back into the burrow.

In the middle of summer Woody digs his own little burrow near his mother's. Later that summer, Woody moves away and digs another burrow, his very own.

Woody's new burrow usually has one big hole with a mound of dirt in front for a main entrance. The mound is his lookout spot, a sunbathing place and an outdoor toilet. Woody also digs three or four small steep holes which are hidden and have no mound. These are his secret back doors. If danger is near, he can use the closest door to escape.

While Woody digs his new home, he must also get ready for winter. All summer he eats grasses, seeds, roots, leaves and fruit and sometimes grasshoppers and June bugs. In early fall Woody is so fat he can hardly hold his stomach off the ground. Soon he shuts himself up in his bedroom. His body gets cold, his heart beat is not as rapid, he breathes very slowly and he sleeps so deeply you wouldn't be able to wake him even if you shook him. He uses his stored fat for food, and he sleeps until March. This is called *hibernation* (hy bur NAY shun).

When Woody is two years old, he will be grown up and a father. When he is six years old, he will be old and gray. As an adult, he will weigh about seven pounds (about 3.2 kilograms) and be about twenty-one inches (about 53.3 centimeters) long. His claws will be heavy and his muscles, strong. His sharp rodent's teeth, like those of the beaver or mouse, will grow all his life and he will be a good fighter if cornered. Woody isn't as smart as your dog, but he is alert and quick. Just try to sneak up on old Woody. You'll find out.

	Possible Score	Your Score

1. What would be another good title for this passage?

   ☐ a. Mating Marvels of the Forest
   ☐ b. Life of a Young Woodchuck
   ☐ c. Friendly but Lazy   **15**   ◯
   ☐ d. How Woodchucks Protect Themselves

2. Woody spends the winter

   ☐ a. hibernating.
   ☐ b. looking for food.
   ☐ c. caring for his young.
   ☐ d. mating.   **15**   ◯

3. A newborn woodchuck

   ☐ a. can locate its own food.
   ☐ b. cannot see.
   ☐ c. does not nurse.   **15**   ◯
   ☐ d. is deaf.

4. If an animal is cornered,

   ☐ a. it doesn't have enough food.
   ☐ b. it falls asleep.
   ☐ c. its escape is being blocked.   **15**   ◯
   ☐ d. its nest has been robbed.

5. As used in this passage, greens are

   ☐ a. insects.
   ☐ b. liquids.
   ☐ c. plants.   **15**   ◯
   ☐ d. small animals.

6. Main Idea

	Answer	Score
Mark the main idea	M	(10)
Mark the statement that is a detail	D	(5)
Mark the statement that is too narrow	N	(5)
Mark the statement that is too broad	B	(5)

a. A woodchuck's life is short but very busy. □ ○

b. Some animals are busier than others. □ ○

c. An adult woodchuck weighs about 7 pounds (about 3.2 kilograms). □ ○

d. While digging a home, a woodchuck also gets ready for winter. □ ○

Total Comprehension Score
(Add your scores and enter the total on the graph on page 103.)

Categories of Comprehension Questions

No. 1: Subject Matter	No. 4: Clarifying Devices
No. 2: Supporting Details	No. 5: Vocabulary in Context
No. 3: Conclusion	No. 6: Main Idea

19. The Butterfly Clam

One warm, sunny day I sat by the shore of the Gulf of Mexico. I watched the waves slowly roll up on the beach. The water pushed and pulled at the beach sand. As the sand grains danced about, I saw hundreds of tiny sea shells that were uncovered by the waves.

I reached down to pick up one of the tiny shells. But by the time my fingers were near it, the shell had disappeared. In fact, all the shells had vanished!

I knew that each tiny shell was the home of a living animal called a *mollusk*. The hard shell protects the soft, boneless clam from many foes. I waited for one more wave to wash the sand away. Then, like magic, the shells were there again. As the wave rolled back to the sea, I could see the animals digging back into the wet sand.

I pushed my hand into the sand. When I pulled it out, I had a handful of tiny shells. The shells were almost closed, but I could see some pink parts of the little animals that stuck out and wriggled. Each shell was about three-quarters of an inch (about 1.9 centimeters) across, or smaller. They were beautiful! Some were pink, some brown and yellow. Others were shades of blue and purple. Each was a different color. But all had the same sunburst design.

I watched them wriggle in my hand for a few minutes and then gently put them back in the wet sand. I decided to look for some empty shells that I could take home with me. I hunted for <u>abandoned</u> shells along the beach, and in no time at all I had my hands full of them.

When both halves of one of these little empty shells are open and lying flat, they look like butterfly wings. That's why some people call these sea animals the *butterfly clam*. Another name for this mollusk with a beautiful shell house is the *butterfly coquina* (co KEE nah).

	Possible Score	Your Score

1. The butterfly clam is

   ☐ a. a shellfish.
   ☐ b. a type of squid.
   ☐ c. a plant.
   ☐ d. an insect.   ⑮   ◯

2. How large are the butterfly clams?

   ☐ a. As big as a pinhead
   ☐ b. The size of a dime
   ☐ c. About fist size
   ☐ d. As big as an apple   ⑮   ◯

3. To protect its body, the butterfly clam has

   ☐ a. sharp teeth.
   ☐ b. a stinger.
   ☐ c. strong bones.
   ☐ d. a hard shell.   ⑮   ◯

4. Who is sitting on the shore in the first paragraph?

   ☐ a. A small child
   ☐ b. A sea gull
   ☐ c. A group of nature lovers
   ☐ d. The writer of the passage   ⑮   ◯

5. An abandoned shell is one that has been

   ☐ a. broken.
   ☐ b. given up.
   ☐ c. eaten.
   ☐ d. buried.   ⑮   ◯

6. Main Idea

	Answer	Score
Mark the main idea	M	(10)
Mark the statement that is a detail	D	(5)
Mark the statement that is too narrow	N	(5)
Mark the statement that is too broad	B	(5)

a. The body of the butterfly clam is soft and boneless.

b. Beauty can be seen in the most tiny things.

c. The butterfly clam is a tiny sea animal with a beautiful, colored shell.

d. Some of the butterfly clams are pink, some brown and yellow.

Total Comprehension Score
(Add your scores and enter the
total on the graph on page 103.)

Categories of Comprehension Questions

No. 1: Subject Matter	No. 4: Clarifying Devices
No. 2: Supporting Details	No. 5: Vocabulary in Context
No. 3: Conclusion	No. 6: Main Idea

20. Beware the Web!

The spider climbed to the tip of the branch. There it raised its stomach and began to spin a fine thread that sailed out behind it. The slowly drifting air took the thread to the branch of a nearby shrub where it caught. The spider pulled in the slack and made its end of the thread fast. Now it had a sort of tightrope along which it could walk (upside down, of course) to the next shrub.

For the next few minutes, it busied itself making draglines. These were attached from branch to branch across the spot where it wished to spin its sticky web. Next, it spun a line across the center. From this center line it made many lines like spokes, spacing and connecting each one. Then, starting at the center, it kept spinning its sticky trap with wider and wider circles of silk.

Last, it spun a *trapline*. This is a single thread from the center of the web to a hiding place in the shrub. This thread would send vibrations to it if an insect should get entangled. It would also be its route to the web. Its job was now finished.

The next day was warm. Flies buzzed about. Grasshoppers, leaf hoppers and other small bugs were active. About noon, a grasshopper fell into the newly made trap. At first it seemed as if the grasshopper might escape, so fierce was its struggle. But the sticky threads held. The spider, sensing the movements of the web through its trapline, ran quickly to the grasshopper. At once it spun more silk around the still-struggling insect. There was no chance for escape, but through some instinct it bit the prey with its needle-sharp fang just in case. When it did so, a tiny bit of poison flowed into the grasshopper. It ceased to fight, but it did not die. The poison just <u>paralyzed</u> it. It is much easier to suck the body fluids from a living insect than from a dead and dried up one. The silky trap had done what webs for thousands of years have done. It caught food for its shy but skilled weaver.

	Possible Score	Your Score

1. This passage is mostly about

   ☐ a. different kinds of webs.
   ☐ b. how webs are made.
   ☐ c. fixing old webs.
   ☐ d. the sticky substance of a web.   (15)   ◯

2. A spider feels vibrations from the web through the

   ☐ a. trapline.
   ☐ b. center line.
   ☐ c. draglines.
   ☐ d. body fluids.   (15)   ◯

3. This writer suggests that spiders feed on

   ☐ a. plants.
   ☐ b. dead insects.
   ☐ c. nonflying insects.
   ☐ d. the body fluids of insects.   (15)   ◯

4. The lines of a web are compared to

   ☐ a. a silk thread.
   ☐ b. the branches of trees.
   ☐ c. the links in a chain.
   ☐ d. a maze.   (15)   ◯

5. A paralyzed insect is one that

   ☐ a. struggles.
   ☐ b. makes noise.
   ☐ c. cannot move.
   ☐ d. is dead.   (15)   ◯

6. Main Idea

	Answer	Score
Mark the main idea	M	(10)
Mark the statement that is a detail	D	(5)
Mark the statement that is too narrow	N	(5)
Mark the statement that is too broad	B	(5)

a. The spider has needle-sharp fangs.

b. Some spiders build webs that are sticky.

c. Spider webs are used to trap food.

d. Spider webs are intricate things.

Total Comprehension Score
(Add your scores and enter the
total on the graph on page 103.)

Categories of Comprehension Questions

No. 1: Subject Matter	No. 4: Clarifying Devices
No. 2: Supporting Details	No. 5: Vocabulary in Context
No. 3: Conclusion	No. 6: Main Idea

21. The Flashy Firebird

If you have luck, you might see a scarlet tanager with its fiery feathers. If you do, you will never forget it. In the spring this seven-inch (about 17.8-centimeter) bird arrives. It comes from its winter home in the south blazing with color. The bright red of its body is in strong contrast to the black wings and tail.

Its merry song can be heard far away. People who study birds say that sometimes the scarlet tanager sings a *whisper song*. This means that, though it is a complete or perfect song, it is so faint you can't tell how far away the bird is.

The male scarlet tanager wins his mate by preening in front of her. He droops his wings and puffs up his bright red breast. Once the female is won, she begins to gather twigs, weed stalks and rootlets. With these she builds a nest. She likes to build her nest in the woods near the end of an oak limb. This is about ten to twenty feet (about 3.1 to 6.2 meters) from the ground. She lines her nest with flower stems and vines.

While the female builds, and later while she sits upon her three or four blue-white eggs, the male perches on a nearby limb and chirps away. If danger threatens his mate, he flies to her defense. Then the eggs hatch. The father helps provide food for his offspring.

In the spring, tanagers are often found near the ground looking for berries and flowers. The farmer is happy to see these birds arrive. They do eat some of the seeds of the plants. But tanagers also eat insects that harm the crops. In fact, later in the summer the birds' diet is mostly caterpillars and bugs.

The scarlet tanager juggles berries like an expert. If one slips from its beak while it is flying, it swoops down and catches it right in midair!

The male seems to know that his flashy color makes it easy for him to be seen. He tries to stay mainly in the treetops. But his mate moves about more freely. She sometimes becomes very tame.

Try to get close to a male scarlet tanager. He may surprise you by cocking his head to one side and peering at you for a few moments. Then he will turn his head and stare at you with his other eye. He looks as though he is in doubt about something. Experts tell us that some birds can't see things with both eyes at once since their eyes are on opposite sides of their heads. They cock their heads because they can use just one eye at a time.

There are about 300 kinds of tanagers. Only four, including the scarlet tanager, are found in North America.

?

	Possible Score	Your Score

1. This passage is about a

   ☐ a. fish.
   ☐ b. snake.
   ☐ c. rodent.
   ☐ d. bird.

   (15)   ◯

2. How many species of tanagers are found in North America?

   ☐ a. 1
   ☐ b. 2
   ☐ c. 3
   ☐ d. 4

   (15)   ◯

3. We can see that the male tanager

   ☐ a. will often hurt its mate.
   ☐ b. does not build the nest.
   ☐ c. leaves the female unprotected.
   ☐ d. builds the nest and cares for the eggs.

   (15)   ◯

4. What color are "fiery feathers?"

   ☐ a. Gold
   ☐ b. Red
   ☐ c. White
   ☐ d. Yellow

   (15)   ◯

5. Flashy colors are

   ☐ a. bright.
   ☐ b. dull.
   ☐ c. dirty.
   ☐ d. pale.

   (15)   ◯

6. Main Idea

	Answer	Score
Mark the main idea	M	(10)
Mark the statement that is a detail	D	(5)
Mark the statement that is too narrow	N	(5)
Mark the statement that is too broad	B	(5)

a. Some birds are more attractive than others.

b. The scarlet tanager is a beautiful and interesting bird.

c. The scarlet tanager's fiery feathers blaze with color.

d. The father tanager helps provide food for the young.

Total Comprehension Score
(Add your scores and enter the
total on the graph on page 103.)

Categories of Comprehension Questions

No. 1: Subject Matter	No. 4: Clarifying Devices
No. 2: Supporting Details	No. 5: Vocabulary in Context
No. 3: Conclusion	No. 6: Main Idea

22. Defending Her Young

When autumn came to the forest, it brought frost that killed the plants in the stream. Alces ate more and more twigs and began eating bark from the trees. The twins were weaned by now, which meant they no longer needed Alces' milk. They now shared the same food she ate.

Winter brought heavy snow. Alces and her calves lived on twigs and bark and the fat which they had built up in their bodies during summer. Winter also brought a great quiet to the forest. Many birds had migrated south. But some, such as snowy owls, remained. Lynx, coyotes and the wisest hunters of all, the wolves, still roamed the forest.

One afternoon, when Alces and the calves were looking for food at the edge of a frozen lake, a pack of wolves trotted into view. Alces swung around to face them. The twins moved behind her. The wolves spread out and crouched in a semicircle, waiting. They were too smart to attack Alces, who was a mature, healthy moose. They were after the calves.

Suddenly one wolf dashed forward. Alces swung her great head, and the wolf went flying into the snow! Quickly it ran back to join the others. The standoff between the wolves and Alces continued for almost an hour. Finally, the wolves gave up and trotted away. They would look for easier prey, perhaps an abandoned calf or an ill or old moose.

At long last springtime came to the forest. Alces and the calves, thin from the hard winter, ate the new leaves and watercress. Gradually they got fatter and fatter.

The young moose would stay with their mother until they were two years old. Then Alces would be ready to have a new family. She would drive the twins away to live on their own.

Alces might live for twenty years if she were lucky. But the northern wilderness is not gentle, and few moose die of old age. The important thing is that the adults keep having babies to replace the moose that die. Alces was doing her share of that.

	Possible Score	Your Score

1. What would be another good title for this passage?

   ☐ a. A Home in the Wilderness
   ☐ b. Alces and Her Calves
   ☐ c. The Twins Leave Home
   ☐ d. Alces Becomes a Pet

   15 ◯

2. Young moose stay with their mother for

   ☐ a. 1 month.
   ☐ b. 6 months.
   ☐ c. 1 year.
   ☐ d. 2 years.

   15 ◯

3. The wolves in this passage were most likely

   ☐ a. thirsty.
   ☐ b. looking for a home.
   ☐ c. hungry.
   ☐ d. searching for mates.

   15 ◯

4. Winter brings a great quiet to the forest. The forest becomes

   ☐ a. tense.
   ☐ b. calm.
   ☐ c. busy.
   ☐ d. fidgety.

   15 ◯

5. An ill moose is

   ☐ a. strong.
   ☐ b. gentle.
   ☐ c. sick.
   ☐ d. tidy.

   15 ◯

6. Main Idea

	Answer	Score
Mark the main idea	M	⑩
Mark the statement that is a detail	D	⑤
Mark the statement that is too narrow	N	⑤
Mark the statement that is too broad	B	⑤

a. Moose live in danger of being attacked by wolves in the forest.

b. One winter afternoon Alces had to defend her calves against a pack of wolves.

c. A mother moose fed and protected her calves until they were old enough to live on their own.

d. A moose might live for 20 years.

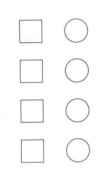

Total Comprehension Score
(Add your scores and enter the total on the graph on page 103.)

Categories of Comprehension Questions

No. 1: Subject Matter	No. 4: Clarifying Devices
No. 2: Supporting Details	No. 5: Vocabulary in Context
No. 3: Conclusion	No. 6: Main Idea

23. Courtship of Golden Eagles

Golden eagles are often seen by the western border of Nebraska. I have always loved these great birds. As a wildlife photographer, I wanted to get a record in pictures of eagles with their young.

Early one spring day I watched a pair of golden eagles. They were courting each other in flight. I knew my chance had come. The birds were only specks in the big western sky. They were flying above a rocky region known as the Wildcat Hills. Through binoculars I watched them <u>soar</u> higher and higher. Soon they leveled off and circled for a while.

Then the lead bird folded its wings and dived toward the earth. Its mate power-dived, too. Only when they were within a few feet of the rocky hills did they stretch their wings and sweep upward. The death-defying dives went on for nearly half an hour. Then the pair flew to a high cliff and settled on a huge pile of sticks — their nest.

A short drive in my car and a half-hour hike brought me to the top of the cliff. There I could look down on the nest. I found a good spot about forty feet (about 12.2 meters) away from the birds. I set up a hiding place there so I could photograph them.

My friend Mike Linch, who lived in a nearby town, agreed to keep watch on the nest. Forty days later he sent word that two eggs had hatched. My picture record could begin.

	Possible Score	Your Score

1. The courtship of the golden eagle takes place

   ☐ a. in a forest.
   ☐ b. in the nest.
   ☐ c. on the ground. ⑮ ◯
   ☐ d. in the air.

2. In this passage, the eagles live in

   ☐ a. Nebraska.
   ☐ b. South Dakota.
   ☐ c. North Dakota. ⑮ ◯
   ☐ d. Manitoba.

3. How long does it take the eagle eggs to hatch?

   ☐ a. 1 week
   ☐ b. 1 month
   ☐ c. 40 days ⑮ ◯
   ☐ d. 60 days

4. A death-defying dive is very

   ☐ a. dangerous.
   ☐ b. slow.
   ☐ c. easy. ⑮ ◯
   ☐ d. colorful.

5. When eagles <u>soar</u>, they are

   ☐ a. dancing.
   ☐ b. walking.
   ☐ c. flying. ⑮ ◯
   ☐ d. eating.

6. Main Idea

	Answer	Score
Mark the main idea	M	⑩
Mark the statement that is a detail	D	⑤
Mark the statement that is too narrow	N	⑤
Mark the statement that is too broad	B	⑤

a. An eagle's nest is usually a huge pile of sticks high on a cliff or tree.

b. One of nature's most beautiful birds attracted a wildlife photographer.

c. A wildlife photographer wanted to make a picture record of the courtship of two golden eagles.

d. The photographer found a good spot about 40 feet (about 12.2 meters) away from the birds.

Total Comprehension Score
(Add your scores and enter the total on the graph on page 103.)

Categories of Comprehension Questions

No. 1: Subject Matter   No. 4: Clarifying Devices

No. 2: Supporting Details   No. 5: Vocabulary in Context

No. 3: Conclusion   No. 6: Main Idea

24. Eggs and Incubation

Mother birds begin to lay eggs a day or two after the nest is built. The chimney swift is an exception. The mates take too long to finish their stick-and-saliva nest. The female will start laying eggs when the nest is half finished. They go on building until the eggs hatch. The birds we see most often lay one egg a day.

As you would guess, the tiny hummingbird lays the smallest eggs. They are about the size of a bean. The largest eggs that you are likely to see are those of the mute swans that nest in parks. They look like a stretched-out baseball. Birds whose young can walk right after hatching lay larger eggs than those with naked, helpless nestlings. A killdeer and a robin are close in size. But the killdeer's eggs are nearly twice as large as the robin's.

As in nest building, the females of common North American species do most of the incubating. An exception is the woodpecker. The male does most of the sitting. Also, with pigeons, cuckoos, owls and starlings, the sexes share the task.

While his mate sits, the male stays near. He protects their territory by singing and watching the boundaries. If the female flies off for food, water or just a rest, he will guard the eggs. Male chickadees, goldfinches and blue jays will feed their sitting mates. This does not mean such birds love their mates more. They do it because their species has always done that.

After sitting for half an hour, a bird gets <u>fidgety</u> and flies off. Birds won't leave eggs uncovered for more than fifteen minutes. The unhatched birds might die if their temperature were to drop as low as 80° Fahrenheit (about 26.7 degrees Celsius).

Most North American garden birds incubate for two weeks. When eggs are about to hatch, the parents can hear peeping sounds inside. Sometimes they help the young ones to emerge. The adults then carry the egg shells far away.

	Possible Score	Your Score

1. What would be another good title for this passage?

   ☐ a. Different Colors of Eggs
   ☐ b. How Eggs Develop
   ☐ c. The Egg Hatching of Birds
   ☐ d. Snake Eggs

   Possible Score: (15) **Your Score:** ◯

2. Which of the following lays the largest egg?

   ☐ a. The mute swan
   ☐ b. The killdeer
   ☐ c. The woodpecker
   ☐ d. The owl

   Possible Score: (15) **Your Score:** ◯

3. After reading this passage, we can see that some nestlings can walk right after birth. They are

   ☐ a. apt to die young.
   ☐ b. less helpless than smaller, naked nestlings.
   ☐ c. usually sickly.
   ☐ d. born naked and helpless.

   Possible Score: (15) **Your Score:** ◯

4. The eggs of a mute swan look like a "stretched-out baseball." This means the eggs look

   ☐ a. short and round.
   ☐ b. square.
   ☐ c. long and oval.
   ☐ d. small and leathery.

   Possible Score: (15) **Your Score:** ◯

5. As used in this passage, <u>fidgety</u> means

   ☐ a. tired.
   ☐ b. hungry.
   ☐ c. lonesome.
   ☐ d. restless.

   Possible Score: (15) **Your Score:** ◯

6. Main Idea

	Answer	Score
Mark the main idea	M	10
Mark the statement that is a detail	D	5
Mark the statement that is too narrow	N	5
Mark the statement that is too broad	B	5

a. Building nests and caring for their eggs are major bird activities.

b. Birds are kept very busy most of the time.

c. Mother birds do most of the egg sitting.

d. Male blue jays will feed their mates that are sitting on eggs.

Total Comprehension Score
(Add your scores and enter the total on the graph on page 103.)

Categories of Comprehension Questions

No. 1: Subject Matter	No. 4: Clarifying Devices
No. 2: Supporting Details	No. 5: Vocabulary in Context
No. 3: Conclusion	No. 6: Main Idea

25. A Coat of Many Colors

One kind, or *species* (SPEE sheez), of bear is *black bear*. It is unlike other species such as polar bears or grizzlies. It is the kind you are most likely to find in a major national park. You can see it begging for food on the side of the road.

The so-called black bear ranges over more of North America than any other large animal. It also wears coats of more colors than any other. You might see one in any shade from jet black to pale blond. Thus, this most common of bears is perhaps the most misnamed of animals.

One summer I spent a month taking pictures of black bears. I would see as many as ten bears in all shades of brown before I found a black bear that was really black. One day I even saw a mother bear with two cute little cubs. One was jet black. The other one was a honey blond.

The black bear gained that name from early settlers in the eastern part of North America. These settlers killed bears to get meat and fur. They also wanted to protect their domestic animals from the bears that liked to eat a pig or a calf. These bears *were* black but for a dark brown nose, or muzzle. Perhaps there were a few white hairs or a white spot on the throat or chest. Even these bears' color varies greatly. I once saw one whose whole chest was pure white.

When people moved west, they saw bears that were many shades of brown. They called these *cinnamon bears*. They thought these bears were another kind or species.

They also saw bears that were black, just like the ones back home. But what puzzled them was that often a brown and black bear would be seen roaming around together. Could it be that the two species crossed?

At last it was found that these bears — eastern and western, blonds, brunettes, redheads — were all one kind. Much like kittens or puppies in the same litter, they simply wore different colors. And so the name by which they were first called became the only one — black bear. The tans, browns, cinnamons and yellows are colors of the same species.

The brown and lighter shades seldom appear in the east. They are most common throughout the Rockies and to the west. In Alaska there are a great many black bears. Most of them really are black in color. But there is, in south Alaska and in parts of Canada, a bear known as the *glacier bear* that isn't black. Its color varies from pale smoke to bluish gray to a dark iron-gray. It is also called a *blue bear*. But black cubs turned up as offspring. This proved it to be just one more of the many-colored black bear species.

?

		Possible Score	Your Score

1. This passage is mostly about

   ☐ a. black bear cubs.
   ☐ b. polar bears and grizzlies.
   ☐ c. the hibernation of black bears.　　　**15**　　⚪
   ☐ d. the different colors of black bears.

2. The black bear is usually found

   ☐ a. mostly in the Arctic regions.
   ☐ b. in South America.
   ☐ c. in Central America.　　　**15**　　⚪
   ☐ d. in much of North America.

3. Some black bears

   ☐ a. are mean and ill tempered.
   ☐ b. accept food from humans.
   ☐ c. will not mate in captivity.　　　**15**　　⚪
   ☐ d. attack other members of their species.

4. A cinnamon-colored bear is

   ☐ a. blond.
   ☐ b. off-white.
   ☐ c. brown.　　　**15**　　⚪
   ☐ d. black.

5. Domestic animals are

   ☐ a. born and raised in the forest.
   ☐ b. mostly found in mountainous areas.
   ☐ c. cared for and raised by humans.　　　**15**　　⚪
   ☐ d. usually found running freely on the prairies.

6. Main Idea

	Answer	Score
Mark the main idea	M	(10)
Mark the statement that is a detail	D	(5)
Mark the statement that is too narrow	N	(5)
Mark the statement that is too broad	B	(5)

a. Within the species of black bear, there is a pale blond bear.

b. The black bear comes in any color, from jet black to blond.

c. Black bears often beg for food on the side of the road.

d. Bears in all species come in many colors.

Total Comprehension Score
(Add your scores and enter the total on the graph on page 103.)

Categories of Comprehension Questions

No. 1: Subject Matter   No. 4: Clarifying Devices

No. 2: Supporting Details   No. 5: Vocabulary in Context

No. 3: Conclusion   No. 6: Main Idea

Acknowledgments

The passages appearing in this book have been reprinted with the kind permission of the following publications and publishers to whom the author is indebted:

Aramco World Magazine, published by The Arabian American Oil Company, New York, New York.

The Communicator, published by the New York State Outdoor Education Association, Syracuse, New York.

The Conservationist, published by the New York State Conservation Department, Albany, New York.

A Cornell Science Leaflet, published by the New York State College of Agriculture and Life Sciences, a unit of the State University, at Cornell University, Ithaca, New York.

Food, The Yearbook of Agriculture, published by the United States Department of Agriculture, Washington, D.C.

Handbook of Nature-Study, published by Comstock Publishing Company, Ithaca, New York.

Kansas Fish & Game, published by the Kansas Forestry, Fish and Game Commission, Pratt, Kansas.

National Wildlife, published by The National Wildlife Federation, Washington, D.C.

Outdoor Oklahoma, published by the Oklahoma Department of Wildlife Conservation, Oklahoma City, Oklahoma.

Pennsylvania Game News, published by the Pennsylvania Game Commission, Harrisburg, Pennsylvania.

Ranger Rick's Nature Magazine, published by The National Wildlife Federation, Washington, D.C.

The Tennessee Conservationist, published by the Tennessee Department of Conservation and the Tennessee Game and Fish Commission.

Answer Key: Book 4

Passage 1:	1.d	2.b	3.c	4.a	5.b	6a.N	6b.D	6c.M	6d.B
Passage 2:	1.c	2.c	3.c	4.b	5.c	6a.D	6b.M	6c.N	6d.B
Passage 3:	1.a	2.b	3.a	4.c	5.a	6a.D	6b.N	6c.M	6d.B
Passage 4:	1.a	2.d	3.b	4.d	5.c	6a.M	6b.B	6c.D	6d.N
Passage 5:	1.c	2.a	3.c	4.d	5.b	6a.M	6b.N	6c.D	6d.B
Passage 6:	1.c	2.a	3.d	4.c	5.b	6a.M	6b.B	6c.D	6d.N
Passage 7:	1.a	2.d	3.b	4.b	5.d	6a.D	6b.N	6c.B	6d.M
Passage 8:	1.c	2.d	3.b	4.d	5.b	6a.M	6b.B	6c.N	6d.D
Passage 9:	1.a	2.b	3.c	4.b	5.a	6a.B	6b.N	6c.D	6d.M
Passage 10:	1.b	2.a	3.a	4.b	5.c	6a.M	6b.D	6c.N	6d.B
Passage 11:	1.d	2.a	3.b	4.d	5.b	6a.B	6b.D	6c.N	6d.M
Passage 12:	1.b	2.b	3.c	4.d	5.a	6a.D	6b.B	6c.M	6d.N
Passage 13:	1.d	2.b	3.a	4.b	5.a	6a.B	6b.M	6c.N	6d.D

Passage 14:   1.a   2.d   3.c   4.b   5.b   6a.**D**   6b.**B**   6c.**M**   6d.**N**

Passage 15:   1.b   2.d   3.c   4.a   5.b   6a.**N**   6b.**M**   6c.**D**   6d.**B**

Passage 16:   1.b   2.c   3.a   4.d   5.c   6a.**B**   6b.**N**   6c.**D**   6d.**M**

Passage 17:   1.c   2.d   3.c   4.a   5.a   6a.**B**   6b.**M**   6c.**D**   6d.**N**

Passage 18:   1.b   2.a   3.b   4.c   5.c   6a.**M**   6b.**B**   6c.**D**   6d.**N**

Passage 19:   1.a   2.b   3.d   4.d   5.b   6a.**D**   6b.**B**   6c.**M**   6d.**N**

Passage 20:   1.b   2.a   3.d   4.a   5.c   6a.**D**   6b.**N**   6c.**M**   6d.**B**

Passage 21:   1.d   2.d   3.b   4.b   5.a   6a.**B**   6b.**M**   6c.**N**   6d.**D**

Passage 22:   1.b   2.d   3.c   4.b   5.c   6a.**B**   6b.**N**   6c.**M**   6d.**D**

Passage 23:   1.d   2.a   3.c   4.a   5.c   6a.**D**   6b.**B**   6c.**M**   6d.**N**

Passage 24:   1.c   2.a   3.b   4.c   5.d   6a.**M**   6b.**B**   6c.**N**   6d.**D**

Passage 25:   1.d   2.d   3.b   4.c   5.c   6a.**N**   6b.**M**   6c.**D**   6d.**B**

Diagnostic Chart (For Student Correction)

Directions: Write your final answers in the *upper* part of the passage block. Then correct your answers using the Answer Key on pages 100 and 101. If your answer is correct, do not make any more marks in the block. If your answer is incorrect, write the letter of the correct answer in the *lower* part of the block.

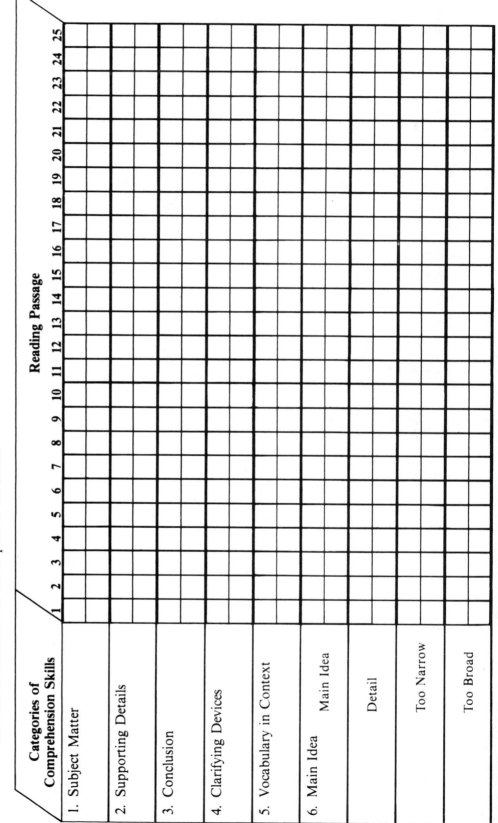

Reading Passage

Categories of Comprehension Skills	1	2	3	4	5	6	7	8	9	10	11	12	13	14	15	16	17	18	19	20	21	22	23	24	25
1. Subject Matter																									
2. Supporting Details																									
3. Conclusion																									
4. Clarifying Devices																									
5. Vocabulary in Context																									
6. Main Idea — Main Idea																									
Detail																									
Too Narrow																									
Too Broad																									

Progress Graph

Directions: Write your Total Comprehension Score in the box under the number for each passage. Then put an *x* along the line above each box to show your Total Comprehension Score for that passage. Then make a graph of your progress. Draw a line to connect the *x*'s.

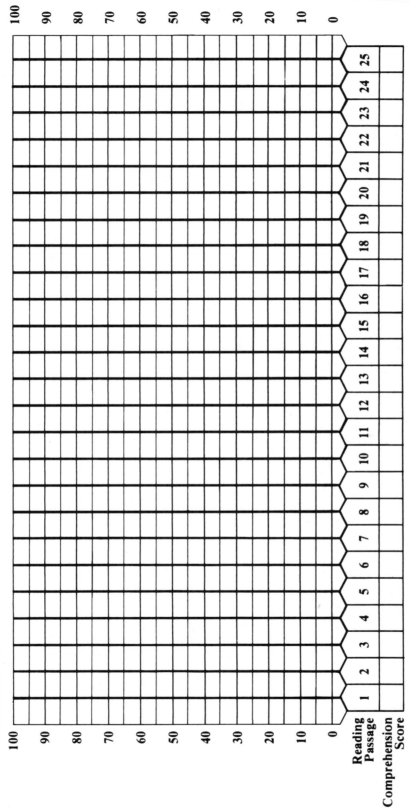
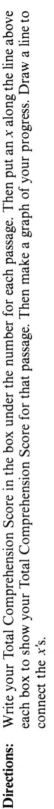

103

Classroom
Management
System

Essential Skills Series

Classroom Management System
(For Teacher Correction)

To the Teacher

The Classroom Management System provides an easy and effective way to individualize instruction. It can be used by reading specialists as well as by regular classroom teachers. The management system is designed to be equally effective when used with a single student, a small group, or a full-size class.

The Classroom Management System provides ongoing assessment of student work for both you and your student. It shows not only the amount of work completed, but also the quality of the work.

It serves as a diagnostic tool by revealing patterns of errors at a glance. For example, if a student has difficulty identifying subject matter (question #1 in each set of questions throughout the *Essential Skills Series*), a pattern of errors will appear in the Subject Matter column of the Classroom Management System Record Sheet. This will enable you to focus on the specific skills needs of each student.

The Classroom Management System Record Sheet is on pages 108-109. Both pages may be duplicated and stapled together.

How to Use the Classroom Management System Record Sheet

Step 1: Have the student answer the questions for each *Essential Skills* passage under the appropriate question heading.

Passage	① Subject Matter	② Supporting Details	③ Conclusion	④ Clarifying Devices	⑤ Vocabulary in Context	⑥ Main Idea				Number Correct	Errors Corrected
						a	b	c	d		
1	d	c	a	b	d			N D B M			

Step 2: Circle any incorrect answers and fill in the total number correct.

1	d	c	a	b	d	(N) D B M	6

106

Step 3: Have the student correct his or her incorrect answers.

1	d	(c) b	a	b	ɔ N (N)(D) B M	6	

Step 4: Give assistance as needed and, if necessary, correct the student's adjusted answers.

1	d	(c) b	a	b	ɔ N (N)(D) B M	6 ✓	

Step 5: Have the student go on to the next passage.

2	b	b	a	d	a	M B N D	

Step 6: Repeat Steps 1–4. If the class is large, it may be necessary to have students complete two or three passages before you correct them. This will slow the "traffic" at your desk.

Note: It is important for students to analyze and, to the extent possible, correct their own errors (Step 3).

Essential Skills Series

Name _____

Teacher _____

Date _____

Book Number _____

Classroom Management System Record Sheet
(For Teacher Correction)

To the Student: Write your answers in the spaces provided. (See the Example below.) Your teacher will circle any incorrect answers. Then go back over the questions and correct your mistakes.

Passage	① Subject Matter	② Supporting Details	③ Conclusion	④ Clarifying Devices	⑤ Vocabulary in Context	⑥ Main Idea a	b	c	d	Number Correct	Errors Corrected
Example	c	(b) a	d	a	c	N (N)	D M	B			
1											
2											
3											
4											
5											
6											
7											
8											
9											
10											

	①		②		③		④		⑤		⑥		
11													
12													
13													
14													
15													
16													
17													
18													
19													
20													
21													
22													
23													
24													
25